INDIAN PIPES

PUSSY LETTERS

By KATE ELENOR WILDER

Nature Stories about Animals, Birds, Insects, Plants, Foods, Textiles, the Forest and the Sea

"How" and "Why"
Stories That Will
Inspire a Love for
Nature and the
Great Out-of-Doors

*One hundred and twenty-nine Illustrations by the Author
Five in Color*

M·A·DONOHUE·&·COMPANY
CHICAGO   MADE IN U.S.A.   NEW YORK

Copyright 1927
Copyright 1929
by
KATE ELENOR WILDER

All rights reserved,
including that of translation into foreign languages
including the Scandinavian

Entered in Stationers Hall
London, England

"Pussy Letters"
are dedicated to the memory of
my grandmother
Ellen Chipman Van Deusen
and to
my beloved mother
who taught me to read every leaf
in Nature's Book.
Through this early training
as a child I realized what it meant
to understand intelligently
nature's great work.

AUTHOR'S NOTE

"Pussy Letters" have been written to awaken the children's interest in the great out-of-doors; to teach them to observe what is going on about them, and to bring them in closer touch with Nature's many little folks.

"Pussy Letters" are based upon scientific facts, with a little moral woven into the stories to impress the child.

I believe that children should be made to realize that each plant, bird, and insect leads its individual life; this means much to Mother Earth. These should not be destroyed as their lives are as much a part of this old world as are the lives of the children.

Hamilton Wright Mabie, in his book "Nature and Culture," says: *"The education imparted by contact with nature is so inclusive, so deep, and so vital, that from this point of view nature seems to exist for the development of man.

"Nature taught men, first of all, to see things and then to make use of them.

"About every man's feet there lies a wonderland of force, life, law, and beauty which has ministered so mysteriously and so vitally to the unfolding life of his race; and that wonderland is open to everyone who is willing to give the eye and the mind the training of observation.

"The knowledge which a man may gain, directly and indirectly, by observation, imagination, absorption, and self surrender from nature makes him an artist in the use and treatment of his life.

"It ought to be as great a reproach to a man not to be able to read the open pages of the world about him as not to be able to read the open pages of the book before him."

Chum, who is the main character in the "Pussy Letters," has been my companion for ten years. He accompanies me on my tramps in the woods, and has traveled all over the country.

*By courtesy of Hamilton Wright Mabie and Dodd, Mead & Co., Inc.

Chum has very big paws. He uses them in "Pussy Letters" to help his little nature friends out of their difficulties.

Bill Grackle, one of the bird characters in "Pussy Letters," was found with a broken leg. We brought him into the house and kept him all one winter. Chum and he became great friends. When spring came we let Billy out and he stayed about our grounds all summer and would often join Chum and me on our walks. He would fly along, stopping when we stopped.

Grackles make a noise like a rusty hinge. We always called that Billy talking to us. He would go away in the winter and come back in the spring to spend the summer with us.

Curley was a pet grey squirrel who was also Chum's friend.

Duke, the St. Bernard, and Diamond were my dogs.

These are some of the real characters in "Pussy Letters."

I love them all and I hope you will.

KATE ELENOR WILDER.

TABLE OF CONTENTS

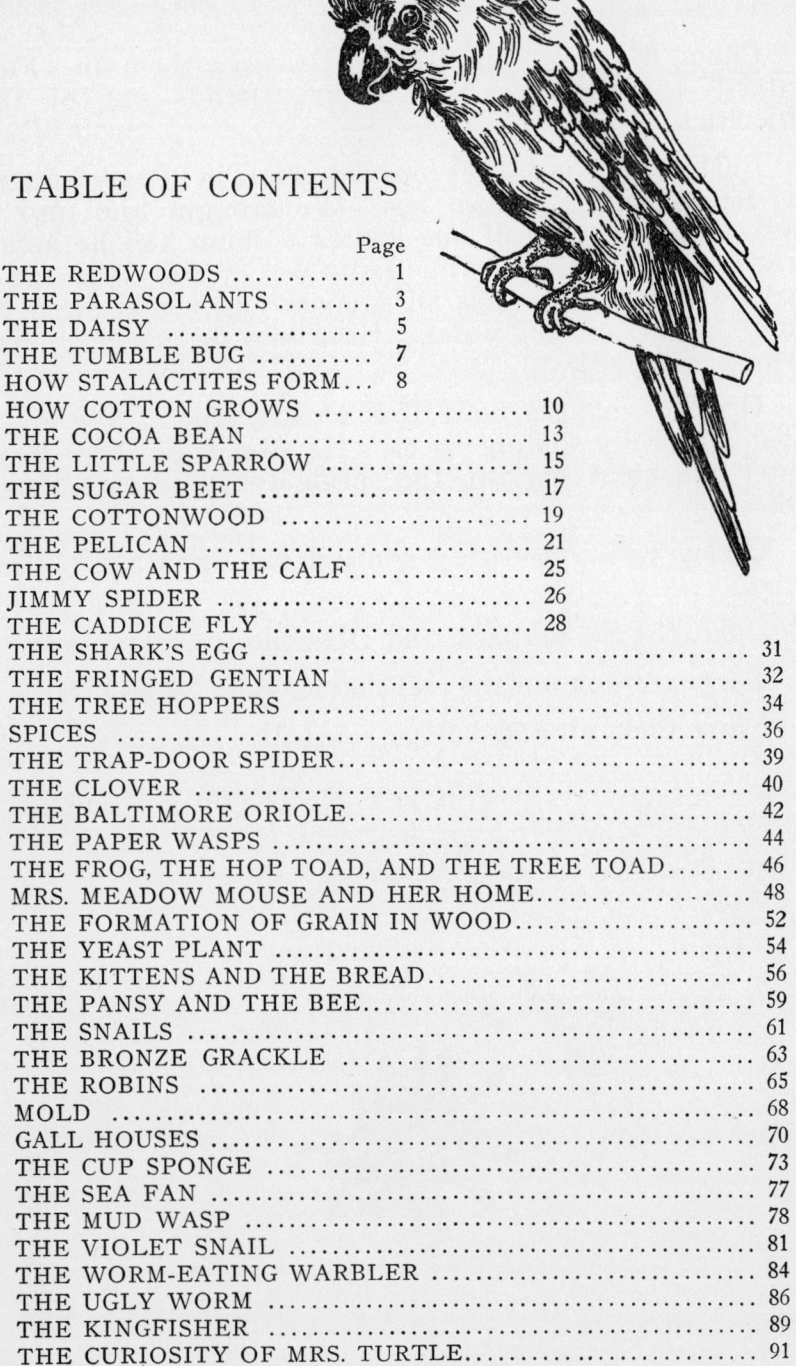

	Page
THE REDWOODS	1
THE PARASOL ANTS	3
THE DAISY	5
THE TUMBLE BUG	7
HOW STALACTITES FORM	8
HOW COTTON GROWS	10
THE COCOA BEAN	13
THE LITTLE SPARROW	15
THE SUGAR BEET	17
THE COTTONWOOD	19
THE PELICAN	21
THE COW AND THE CALF	25
JIMMY SPIDER	26
THE CADDICE FLY	28
THE SHARK'S EGG	31
THE FRINGED GENTIAN	32
THE TREE HOPPERS	34
SPICES	36
THE TRAP-DOOR SPIDER	39
THE CLOVER	40
THE BALTIMORE ORIOLE	42
THE PAPER WASPS	44
THE FROG, THE HOP TOAD, AND THE TREE TOAD	46
MRS. MEADOW MOUSE AND HER HOME	48
THE FORMATION OF GRAIN IN WOOD	52
THE YEAST PLANT	54
THE KITTENS AND THE BREAD	56
THE PANSY AND THE BEE	59
THE SNAILS	61
THE BRONZE GRACKLE	63
THE ROBINS	65
MOLD	68
GALL HOUSES	70
THE CUP SPONGE	73
THE SEA FAN	77
THE MUD WASP	78
THE VIOLET SNAIL	81
THE WORM-EATING WARBLER	84
THE UGLY WORM	86
THE KINGFISHER	89
THE CURIOSITY OF MRS. TURTLE	91

TABLE OF CONTENTS—Continued

	Page
THE ANT COWS	94
SPIDERS BALLOONING	96
FIRE FLIES	98
THE AUTUMN RACE	100
THE ROSE MALLOW	102
EXAMINATION AT THE BIRD SCHOOL	104
RUBBER	107
THE DESERTED VILLAGE	109
THE CICADA OR SEVENTEEN-YEAR LOCUST	111
THE SILKWORM	113
THE BEE'S BREAD BASKET	115
THE MARSH MALLOW	117
THE SWORDFISH	119
THE GREAT BLUE HERON	121
THE CREAM THIEF	123
THE EARTHWORM	125
MAPLE SUGAR	128
HOW BULBS GROW	131
THE LEAF BUD	135
THE DRAGON FLY	137
THE ACCOMMODATING RATS	141
TEA	142
DAHLIAS	144
THE DOWNY WOODPECKER	146
THE DANDELION	148
THE RED-HEADED WOODPECKER	150
THE RUBY-THROATED HUMMING BIRD	152
THE TADPOLES AND THE MOSQUITOES	154
THE MINER WASPS	157
HEMP	158
JACK-IN-THE-PULPIT	160
THE HORSESHOE CRAB	162
THE YELLOW-BILLED CUCKOO	165
WHAT ONE SHOULD KNOW ABOUT A SEED	166
WHEN WE PLANT SEEDS	168
THE BLUE JAY	170
THE HERMIT CRAB	172
FOSSILS	174
THE BAT	176
HOW COFFEE GROWS	178
THE MONARCH BUTTERFLY	180
CURLEY AND THE BUTTERNUT TREE	182
THE CLAM FAMILY	185
HOW SEEDS TRAVEL	187
THE CROW AND THE CORN	190

LIST OF ILLUSTRATIONS

	Page
THE SPIKED OYSTER	vi
THE PARROT	vii
THE PIGEONS	xii
THE REDWOODS	xiv
THE CHIMNEY SWALLOW	2
THE PARASOL ANTS	3
THE DAISY	5
THE TUMBLE BUGS	7
THE STALACTITE CAVE	9
LIFE HISTORY OF THE COTTON PLANT	11
THE COCOA TREE	12
THE COCOA BLOSSOM, POD, AND BEAN	14
MAGNIFIED HEAD OF ANT	14
THE SPARROW	16
THE SUGAR BEET	18
THE PELICAN	21
THE SPIDER AND HER EGG SAC	22
THE SHEPHERD DOG AND HIS SHEEP	23
THE CALF	24
JIMMY SPIDER	26
BILL GRACKLE AND THE SPIDERS	27
LIFE HISTORY OF THE CADDICE FLY	29
SHARK'S EGG, THE	31
THE FRINGED GENTIAN	33
THE TREE HOPPERS	34
THE TREE HOPPER'S EGG CUPS	35
NUTMEG, VANILLA BEAN, ALLSPICE, AND CLOVE	37
THE TRAP-DOOR SPIDER	38
THE CLOVER	40
THE BALTIMORE ORIOLE'S NEST	42
THE PAPER WASPS' NEST	44
THREE WASPS' NESTS	45
FROG'S EGGS, TADPOLE, AND TOAD'S EGGS	47
MRS. MEADOW MOUSE AND HER TIN CAN HOUSE	49

LIST OF ILLUSTRATIONS—Continued

	Page
THE FAMILY CIRCLE	51
GRAIN IN WOOD	53
MAGNIFIED YEAST PLANTS	55
KITTENS IN THE BREAD DOUGH	57
PUSSY WILLOWS	58
WHEN CHUM WAS STUNG BY A BEE	59
THE PANSY AND THE BEE	60
TWO SNAILS AND A SLUG	62
BILL GRACKLE ON THE LECTURE STAND	64
THE ROBIN FAMILY	66
GROWING MOLD PLANT, MAGNIFIED	69
OAK GALLS	71
THE CUP SPONGE	72
CORAL POLYPS, BRANCH CORAL, AND BRAIN CORAL	74
THE SPIDER CRAB	75
THE LADY CRAB	75
THE SHRIMP	75
THE SEA FAN	76
THE MUD WASPS	79
A GROWING SPONGE	80
THE VIOLET SNAIL	82
THE SEA GULL	83
THE HICKORY HORN-DEVIL AND THE SPHINX WORM	85
THE CECROPIA WORM	87
THE CECROPIA MOTH	88
THE CRADLE COCOON	88
THE KINGFISHER	90
THE TURTLE	92
LIFE HISTORY OF THE ORNITHOPTERA AMPHRISTUS	93
ANTS AND APHIDS ON BOX ELDER	95
MAGNIFIED ANT MILKING HER COW	95
SPIDERS BALLOONING	97
FIRE FLIES	99
AUTUMN LEAVES AND CATERPILLAR	101
THE ROSE MALLOW	102
THE BIRD SCHOOL	105
THE RUBBER TREE	107

LIST OF ILLUSTRATIONS—Continued

	Page
THE DESERTED VILLAGE OF CICADA	109
THE CICADA	110
THE CICADA AND ITS SHELL ON TREE	111
SILKWORM, EGGS AND MOTH ON MULBERRY TREE	113
SILKWORM COCOON AND MOTH	114
THE BEE'S POLLEN POCKETS	115
THE MALE HERCULES BEETLE	116
THE MARSH MALLOW	117
THE OLEANDER HAWK MOTH	118
THE CRAWFISH	121
THE GREAT BLUE HERON	122
THE COLLIE DOG	124
THE EARTH WORMS	126
THE AMERICAN LARCH	127
OLD BOB AND THE SUGAR MAPLE TREE	129
THE JELLYFISH	130
DAFFODIL, TULIP, NARCISSUS, AND SECTION OF BULB	132
HOW A BULB INCREASES	133
THE LEAF BUD OF HORSE CHESTNUT (MAGNIFIED SECTION)	134
HORSE CHESTNUT BUD, HORSESHOE LEAF SCAR, LEAF BLOSSOM, BURR, AND NUT	136
LARVA OF THE DRAGON FLY	138
THE DRAGON FLY	139
THE RATS AND THE EGG	140
THE TEA PLANT	143
DAHLIA BULBS	145
THE DOWNY WOODPECKER	147
THE FIELD DANDELION	148
THE DANDELION ON THE LAWN	149
THE RED-HEADED WOODPECKER	151
THE HUMMING BIRD'S NEST	153
GRANDFATHER FROG AND THE TADPOLES	154
A SINGING TREE TOAD	155
THE MINER WASPS' NEST	156
CHUM AND THE ROPE	158
JACK-IN-THE-PULPIT	161

LIST OF ILLUSTRATIONS—Continued

	Page
THE HORSESHOE CRAB	162
THE LITTLE CHICKENS	163
MR. AND MRS. YELLOW-BILLED CUCKOO	164
LITTLE MISS WREN	169
THE BLUE JAY	171
THE HERMIT CRAB	173
THE FOSSIL CRINOID	175
THE BAT	177
HOW COFFEE GROWS	179
THE MONARCH BUTTERFLY, AND THE MILKWEED	180
THE OAK LEAF	181
CURLEY AND THE BUTTERNUT TREE	183
THE CANADA THISTLE	184
THE CLAM FAMILY	185
CLAMS SPOUTING WATER	186
HOW SEEDS TRAVEL	188
THE ARCIPUS BUTTERFLY, THE BACK SWIMMER, AND THE POND LILY	189
THE CROW AND THE CORN	191
THE FOX TAIL PINE	192

COLOR ILLUSTRATIONS
Painted by Kate Elenor Wilder

INDIAN PIPES (color plate opposite page)	i
FROG, HOP TOAD AND TREE TOAD (color plate opposite page)	46
WORM EATING WARBLER'S NEST (color plate opposite page)	84
TWO TEACHERS AT THE BIRD SCHOOL (color plate opposite page)	104
KINDERGARTEN SINGING CLASS AT THE BIRD SCHOOL (color plate opposite page)	166

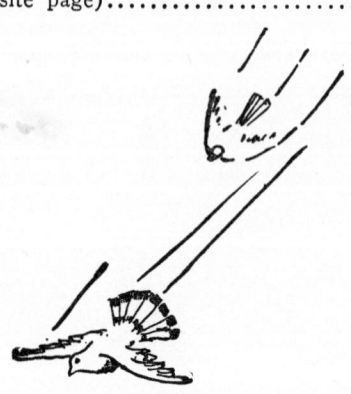

"ARE THEY REALLY GOING TO CUT YOU DOWN?" I ASKED THE REDWOOD

THE REDWOODS

Dear Pussy Cousin:

We are in California. Yesterday I visited one of the great redwood forests. Some of these trees grow to be one hundred and fifty feet high. They stood, with their great arms extended, as though they said: "We have lived for hundreds of years and command the whole world." In a way they do control the world. Do you realize what this world would be if there were no trees? The tree contributes more to man's comfort than any other growing thing.

It awed me as I walked through the forest. I was horrified to see that they were cutting down these great trees. One had been cut and lay on the ground while another was marked to be sawed. As I gazed up at it I could not help crying.

The redwood looked down upon me and said, "What is your name, pussy?"

"Chum," I answered. "Are they really going to cut you down? That is why I am crying."

"You must not cry," the redwood said. "I have fulfilled my purpose on this earth. This forest is full of my children. I scatter my seeds and they come up as happy little trees that grow to be big ones."

"When I stop to think of the many boys and girls, with their papas and mammas whom I have made happy, who have looked up into my branches and have felt nearer to God for doing so, I feel that my life has been worth while.

"Chum, you must not be sad because I am going to be cut down. Perhaps some of my wood will be put into a piece of furniture that you will have in your home, or the boards that are sawed from my great body will be used to build or trim your house. So you can think of me as making others happy."

"Look at the end of that fallen log, Chum," said the redwood. "Do you see those rings? There is one ring that has been made every year since that tree started to grow. The difference in the width of the rings is made by the weather. A wet, good growing season shows a wide ring, while a narrow ring means a dry, short growing season. Now cheer up, pussy, I am as happy as the lark that perched on my branch this morning and sang so sweetly.

"When the wind blows my branches back and forth, I send little messages all through the forest to tell my grandchildren how to live and make themselves noble trees, that will grow straight and clean into the sky. They send me back little kisses on the wind and say, 'Grandma, we are taking your advice. We will try to do just as you have told us,'" said the redwood.

"I will tell you a secret, Chum," said the redwood. "After I am cut down I will send out new shoots that will grow into many branches. They will not be as straight as I am now; but they will laugh as they come up out of my heart."

"Thank you," I said, "for telling me your secret. After you are cut down I am going to watch your stump and when the little sprouts come up, I will whisper to them and tell them that they must be as wonderful as you were."

I was sad as I said good-bye to the great tree, because I knew that I should never see it standing there again.

I will write you more about the forest later.
Good night,
Chum.

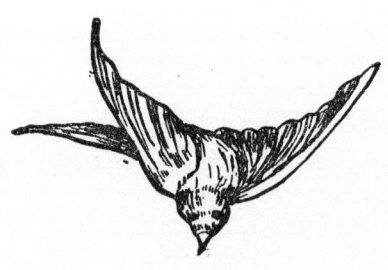

THE PARASOL ANTS

Dear Pussy Cousin:

When we were in Texas, I met the most interesting colony of ants. They are called the parasol ants or leaf cutters.

When I first saw them I could hardly believe my eyes. Going up the side of the hill was an army of ants, one back of another, each carrying a piece of leaf over its head, like a

PARASOL ANTS GOING TO THEIR NEST

parasol. As it was a very hot day, I thought that they were doing it to shade themselves from the sun.

I stopped one ant and asked it what they were doing.

"We are carrying these pieces of leaves to our nest," said the ant. "Come with me and I will show you what we do with them." I followed it back to the tree. Marching up and down it were these large black ants. I could see one of them cutting a leaf. Its jaws worked just like a pair of scissors. It cut out a piece of leaf about the size of a dime. Down it came with the piece of leaf in its mouth. The leaf hung over the ant's head like a parasol. The ant asked me if I would like to go with it to its nest.

I said, "Yes," and followed it.

We came to a mound of soil about two feet high and three feet in diameter. In the center was a hole. These ants were carrying the leaves to the side of the hill, where they left them and went back for more.

Out of the hill came an ant. It picked up a piece of leaf from the pile and carried it down into the hole. My friend, the ant, told me that after they took the leaves down the hole they chewed them to a pulp and used them to fertilize their underground mushroom garden.

"What!" I exclaimed, "Have you a garden under the ground?"

"Indeed we have," said the ant. "In these warm climates vegetation dries up. We ants are very wise and grow food under the ground, where there is moisture, so that our garden does not dry up."

"How wonderful," I said.

"Yes, it is wonderful," said the ant. "At one time people thought that we carried these leaves to line our nests."

"We grind the leaves with our strong jaws into a fine pulp. Into this pulp we put a spore or seed of the mushroom. We grow these mushrooms underground very much as man cultivates the mushrooms in cellars. We use the fine white threads that grow from the mushroom spore or seed as food for our babies and ourselves," said the ant.

"We have our mushroom garden deep under the ground, where we raise plenty of food to last us the whole year, no matter how dry it is," said the ant.

"The natives can tell what kind of a growing season they are going to have, by the number of leaves we cut," said the ant. "When there is going to be a severe drought we know it, and our workers are instructed to cut a great many leaves."

"How does your ant house look under ground?" I asked.

"We have a long central hall with rooms opening into it. When the queen lays her eggs, they are taken into these chambers. The little ants are fed on the mushrooms, which makes them very strong. They have to chew them, and this develops their cutting jaws."

I never realized before how many different kinds of ants there were until I commenced watching them.

Good night,
Chum.

THE DAISY

Dear Pussy Cousin:

This morning while out walking, I stopped in front of two clumps of daisies and heard an interesting conversation. One daisy was selfish and the other was unselfish. The selfish daisy was an only child, whose parents had been picked when she was quite young. She had been brought up by her

grandmother and grandfather, who had devoted their entire time to her.

Had she given them anything in return for their care and attention? No, she had not. Her selfish little face showed it. She stood erect, turned toward the morning sun. Her gown was clean and white from its bath in the dew.

Her poor grandfather was stooped and bent, while her grandmother's dress was torn and shabby.

"Mercy," said the proud, selfish little daisy, to the daisy that grew near her. "You would have as beautiful a gown as mine, if you did not take all your dew drops and shake them on your three sisters."

"Perhaps that is so," answered the unselfish daisy. "My parents were broken off by a thoughtless boy and left to die in the sun. They asked me to take care of my three little sisters. They need all of the moisture that they can get this hot weather. I love to see their jolly little faces turned up for a drink when I shake my dew drops upon them."

I realized for the first time how beautiful her face was. It was all aglow with the happiness of doing for others; so different from the selfish daisy's face.

Grandpa Daisy then said, "I have watched that little daisy make her sacrifices. Perhaps it is our fault that our little granddaughter has the selfish disposition that she shows."

"Why, grandpa, do you think that I am selfish?" asked the daisy. "If I had not taken your dew drops and all of the nourishment from the ground, would you and grandma be as beautiful as Mr. and Mrs. Oxeye Daisy? I shall try to be unselfish. I am not a naughty girl at heart, but just thoughtless.

"Oh, please, Mr. Chum, do not tell anyone what a selfish daisy I have been. Come back and visit me again and you will see how I have changed now that I realize how selfish I am."

I told her that I was very proud of her for acknowledging that she was in the wrong, for it takes a noble character to do that.

Good night,
Chum.

THE TUMBLE BUG

Dear Pussy Cousin:

While going up the country road today, I saw a curious sight. A large black beetle was rolling, or rather pushing, a ball of manure. He was trying to get it out of the wagon track.

I lifted the ball out of the wheel rut with my big paws.

"Thank you," said Mr. Tumble Bug, as he started pushing the ball up the hill.

Mrs. Tumble Bug then said, "It always makes me so proud that my husband takes his share of the responsibility."

She then bade us good-bye, opened up the folding doors of her shell house, drew forth her wings, and flew away to join Mr. Tumble Bug, whom we could see in the distance.

I turned to Bill Grackle and asked him what the tumble bug was going to do with the ball. This is what he told me.

"He will roll that ball up the hill to a dry place to get rid of the many insects that frequent these masses of manure in order to eat the larvae which live there. When he finds the spot that suits him, his wife will lay an egg in the side of the ball. They will then bury it. This ball serves as food for the young tumble bug after it hatches."

"The tumble bug's egg hatches out as a larva. This larva grows to be a thick fleshy grub that lives in the ground. Later it goes into the pupa state and then comes up out of the ground as the beetle which we call a tumble bug."

Good night,
Chum.

HOW STALACTITES FORM

Dear Pussy Cousin:

We have just visited one of the famous caves in Virginia. I wish I had the power to make you see the wonders of this cave.

As we entered, the great stalactites hanging from the rocks looked like huge icicles. The entire cave was lighted by electricity, which made the crystals glisten and shine.

My master said that the stalactites were formed by the water in the cave, which drips over the limestone and slowly evaporates, leaving a column of lime.

The cave was a series of great chambers, each one more beautiful than the other. One of them was called the cathedral, with an altar and candle sticks made of stalactites. The columns in the cathedral, which are called stalagmites, were formed on the floor of the cave in the same manner as the stalactites.

In the cave ball room a great crystal chandelier, formed of stalactites and lighted by electricity, glistened like so many diamonds.

The floor of the cave was solid rock. My master said that this cave went under the mountain, but had been explored for about a half a mile only. I would have gone farther, wouldn't you?

We were going to take the sleeper that night, so we had to go back to the hotel. How I did hate to leave. The wonderful sight will stay with me forever. I can close my eyes now and see the glistening crystals.

I have not told you and Aunt Polly about my new traveling case. It is black leather and looks like a hand bag. It has wire netting at one end with a little curtain that shuts down and covers me all up. My master carries it as if it were a hand satchel, so the porters do not know that I am inside.

I DID NOT WANT TO LEAVE THIS WONDERFUL CAVE

It is great fun. I lie perfectly quiet until we get settled in our compartment.

I will write you about going through the state of South Carolina, where we will see cotton growing.

Good night,
Chum.

HOW COTTON GROWS

Dear Pussy Cousin:

Did you ever stop to think, when you see your mistress in her pretty cotton gown, that it came from a plant?

I never did until we went through South Carolina, where we visited a cotton plantation.

Down there, the cotton grows on a low, bushy plant about three feet high. The blossom is a soft, creamy yellow. While the flower is developing, the cotton is forming in the little boll. This boll grows larger and larger, forcing the petals of the flower up and up until they drop off. When the boll becomes ripe it bursts open. The cotton is then damp and sticky, but as the sun dries it out it becomes fluffy and white.

I touched one of the bolls with my big paw and pulled out a piece of cotton. The negro who was picking the cotton told my mistress that I ought to be able to pick a lot with my big paws and that I had better stay and help them gather the cotton crop.

No inventor has ever been able to make a machine that will pick cotton as well as it can be picked by hand.

I whispered to one of the cotton bolls as we left the field that it was the most beautiful thing that I had ever seen; that because of seeing it I was going to have a great deal more respect for the thread in my mistress's work basket. I will never pull it out again and bat it around with my big paw. I will lift it very carefully and say to it, "Cotton thread, I have seen the cotton plant. It had a beautiful blossom."

My mistress said that man's creative brain has taken this little plant and made of it all of the beautiful cotton materials that are now on the market. He has made cotton one of the great crops of the world.

Good night,
Chum.

THE LIFE HISTORY OF THE COTTON PLANT
THE BUD, FLOWER, BOLL, RIPE COTTON, BALE OF COTTON, AND SPOOL OF COTTON

HOW COCOA PODS GROW ON THE CACAO TREE

THE CACAO BEAN

Dear Pussy Cousin:

You will never be able to guess what Mrs. S. will take out of the box that my mistress is sending her this morning, so I am going to write you just what it is. It is a cacao pod that holds the beans from which cocoa and chololate are made. I saw it growing on the tree when we were in the West Indies.

The curious thing about the cacao tree is that it flowers and forms its pods on the trunk of the tree. This is the only tree that fruits from the trunk. Usually a tree fruits from the branch, you know; but the cacao tree is quite individual in its way of doing things. The flowers start from the trunk of the tree about a foot from the ground, and are very insignificant looking, yet they are fragrant, and dainty. They are a deep pink, have long stamens, and form the pods which contain the beans.

This pod is reddish brown, and is heavy. I think that is why it is necessary for it to form on the trunk of the tree. The tree supports the weight of the pod, whereas if it fruited so heavily on the branch it would break off.

When we went out to see the cacao trees that morning, I was homesick. I sat down under one of the trees and looked up at the curious pods hanging from its trunk and large branches. I touched one with my big paw, and the beans inside rattled. I looked up and there was a big caterpillar looking down at me. "Oh, how glad I am to see you," I said.

My mistress said that the cacao pod protects the bean, but it is not shipped with the beans to cocoa and chocolate manufacturers. When the pods become ripe, they burst open and the beans drop out. The natives dry and ship these beans in sacks to the manufacturers who grind the beans into a paste to make chocolate or cocoa.

The cacao bean also contains a large proportion of a very rich and nutritive oily substance which is called cacao butter. There is a difference between cocoa and chocolate.

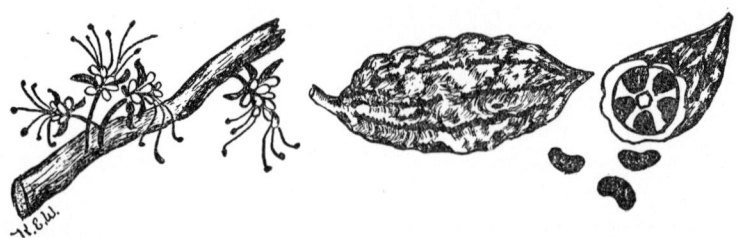

THE FLOWER, THE POD AND THE BEAN OF THE CACAO TREE

This oil is extracted from the cocoa, but is put back to make chocolate. Now when you see your mistress drinking cocoa, or chocolate you will know that it is made from the bean of the cacao tree.

Good night,
Chum.

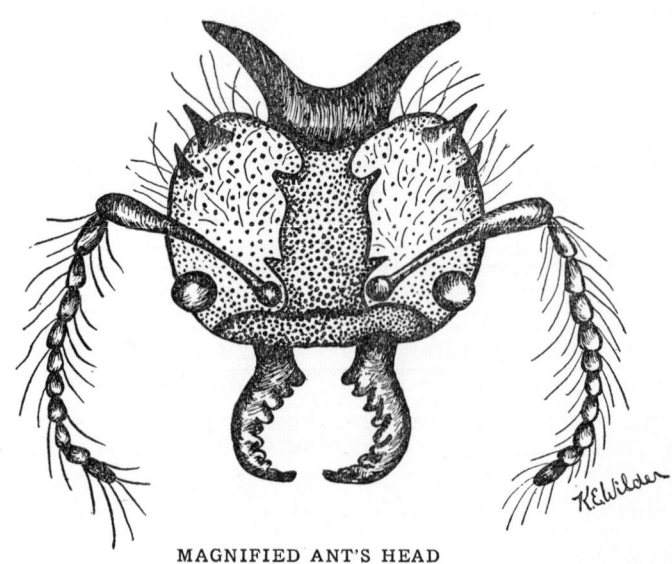

MAGNIFIED ANT'S HEAD

THE LITTLE SPARROW

Dear Pussy Cousin:

My mistress motored into the city today to shop. She took me in the car with her. I love to sit up on the seat and look out of the window.

I noticed for the first time the little sparrows trying to find something to eat in the city streets and on the sidewalks. I saw why it is that they prefer the crowded city streets to the parks and the country.

"Chirp, chirp," said a little sparrow as it looked up into the car from the sidewalk as we stopped.

The chauffeur took a few crackers out of a bag and threw them on the sidewalk.

"Chirp, chirp," said the sparrow to thank him, while a number of other sparrows joined it. After eating the crackers, the other sparrows flew away; but the first sparrow stayed on the sidewalk and gave the people who passed a cheery little chirp.

Along came a man who was haggard and looked as though he was greatly distressed over business or money matters. "Chirp, chirp," said the little sparrow as it looked up into the man's face. The whole expression of the man's face changed as he smiled down at the little sparrow, as much as to say, "You have given me a new hope, with your cheery note."

The next person who came along was a woman whose face had a hard and hopeless expression. "Chirp, chirp," said the little sparrow. She stopped and looked with longing eyes at it. It again chirped to her, and she, too, went away with a smile and softer lines about her face.

The little bird hopped along the crowded street, making others realize that there was something in life beside all of this bustle and worry; that somewhere there were trees with birds singing happily and that these tired people, if they would seek the comfort of the forest, would find happiness there.

The cheery little sparrow, who lives in the crowded city streets, chirps to the poor children and the people who perhaps would never see or think of a bird if it were not for the sparrow. So God has placed the little sparrows in the great city, where their friendly chirp may give happiness to the weary people.

Good night,
Chum.

"CHIRP, CHIRP," SAID THE LITTLE SPARROW

After reading this story, instead of throwing your crusts of bread away, break them up and give them to the birds. These crumbs of comfort will help the little sparrows to give their cheery chirp, that means so much to your city and its people.

Kate Elenor Wilder.

THE SUGAR BEET

Dear Pussy Cousin:

One of the most interesting things that I have seen on my trip was the sugar beet.

You know the big beets that the farmers feed to the cattle? They are raised in large quantities about here and taken to the sugar houses to make beet sugar. It is like the cane sugar, but is sweeter and the grain is finer.

The beets were much larger than any I have ever seen and a different shape. They are longer, more like a carrot.

The big sugar beet told me some of its history. In 1747 a German chemist found a way to extract sugar from beets. There was very little sugar in the beet then.

Sugar beets are now one of the most profitable crops grown. For a great many years they were not appreciated and were fed to cattle. Now they hold their rightful position in the world.

The sugar beet and the sugar cane are the principal sugar producers of the world. The rock maple yields maple sap which is made into maple sugar.

The sugar beet told me that the beet has become more important to the sugar industry than the sugar cane.

The beets are much easier grown and are sweeter. They can be put into a cold storage plant and will still hold their sweetness, while the sugar cane has to be pressed immediately or it will dry out.

Sugar is generally distributed in the vegetable world. Almost all plants contain sugar at some stage of their growth.

Sugar is one of the first substances manufactured by the plant from water and the carbonic acid gas of the atmosphere.

Sugar is necessary to the growth of a plant. It can be formed only when the weather is warm and the sun is shining. Plants manufacture more sugar than they want for their immediate needs, putting the surplus away for future use. This reserve is not always stored away as sugar, but is converted first into starch and then changed back into sugar as it is needed. Some plants that have starch reserves are wheat, rice, barley and potatoes; while others keep their reserve food as sugar.

The roots of the carrot, parsnip, and beet contain sugar made during the first year of the plant's growth. This sugar is used, by the plant, during the second year when it is in blossom.

The sugar from these factories of Dame Nature is utilized by man, for he obtains beet sugar, cane sugar and maple sugar from them.

Good night,
Chum.

THE BIG SUGAR BEET
USED
IN THE MANUFACTURE
OF SUGAR

THE COTTONWOOD

Dear Pussy Cousin:

I went out very early this morning and stood under a big cottonwood tree. I rubbed against the tree, and asked it whether it realized that there was no other tree that had such beautiful white fluffy seeds. I told it that I was surprised to find it here, for there is not another cottonwood tree anywhere in this section.

"Would you like to know how I came to be here?" asked the tree.

This is what the cottonwood tree told me:

"I was born in Kansas, where my mother scattered her seeds to the wind, whispering to it: 'I am sending my children out into the world with you to increase the cottonwood family, so blow them far, far, away, kind wind.'

"I looked at my mother as she stood there scattering her seed to the wind and made up my mind that I would grow to be a great tree and try to be as noble as she.

"I was frightened when I started on my long journey, and held tight to my brothers and sisters that came from the same catkin.

"We sped over a great city. On and on and on we went with the wind. As I looked down I could see that we were crossing a river. It made me dizzy to see the sparkling water below, and I was afraid that the wind would not carry us safely across.

"Coming down the river was a boat. We dropped down to the boat's wheel house, for the wind was not strong enough to keep us sailing up in the air. We landed safely in a corner, so thankful that we were in this sheltered spot. After a rest we wanted to feel the soil, take root, and grow to be trees. But there was nothing but the dry, hard wood of the floor and not a drop of moisture.

"Soon a man came along in a white suit with a broom and swept us out of our corner. The wind caught us and away up in the air we went again, holding tightly to each other.

"Across the river we settled down on the ground, where my brother and sister took root. They said that they were going to stay by the river where they would get plenty of moisture and grow to be big trees.

"I was restless and wanted to see more of the world and to feel that sensation of speeding through the air again into the unknown. So instead of putting a tiny root down into the soft earth I stayed on top where I would keep dry and fluffy, so that the first breeze would pick me up again.

"I was soon riding through the air again. The wind died down and I fell and lodged between some luggage on the running board of an automobile, where I was very glad to rest. It was a new sensation to spin along on an auto, and I enjoyed it.

"After a three days' journey the car turned into a drive with stately trees on each side. I heard the people in the car say, 'Home at last.'

"Someone removed the luggage and I blew away in the soft rich earth. What a wonderful place to live, I thought, as I looked up at the beautiful trees all about me. I made up my mind then and there that I would take root and grow.

"That night it rained and by morning I had sent a tiny little root down into the wet soil. I threw off my soft downy coat and was soon firmly anchored so that the wind could not pick me up and carry me off again.

"I have tried to be a big noble tree like my mother and to give to the people the great happiness that the cottonwood with its shower of fluffy cotton seed gives to everyone who sees the seeds floating in the air on their gay journey to the place where they will land and take root."

So you see, Cousin Ted, when you look at the little fluffy cottonwood floating through the air, you do not realize what a long journey it may take; that perhaps one of these fluffy white seeds may influence the life of a man.

I wonder whether mother cottonwood, as she proudly scatters her seed to the wind, realizes her great life work.

Good night,

Chum.

THE PELICAN

Dear Pussy Cousin:

I happened to think last night as I lay in my basket that I had never written you about the white pelican, which we watched fishing in a river when we were South.

THE PELICAN BACK FROM A FISHING TRIP

This bird is a great fisherman and stows away its fish in a pouch or sac fastened to its flat bill. It not only puts the fish in this pouch to carry home to its young, but while on its fishing trips it seems to realize that there is another dinner hour coming and so it places enough fish in this sac to last for another meal.

Its eyes are very sharp. It combs its feathers back from its smooth round forehead, but allows them to stick out in the back, a habit which would distress the close-cropped, bobbed-haired girl of today.

The pelican is a large web-footed water bird, being five feet long. Its wings measure eight to nine feet from tip to tip.

The pelican is widely distributed in warm climates. Some species migrate to Canada for the summer, but fly back to the South in the fall and are settled for the winter by October.

This big white pelican, after catching its fish and stowing them away in its pouch, came along the beach to a big open nest made of grass, where it fed the fish to three baby pelicans.

My mistress told the children that the pelican also carries water to its young in this pouch, and that the papa pelican sometimes carries food or water to his mate so that she will not have to leave her eggs uncovered in the nest.

The eggs of the pelican vary in number from one to four, and are a creamy or bluish white. They measure three and a half inches long and two and a quarter inches wide.

The plumage of this pelican was very beautiful. It was a clear white, although some species of pelicans are a brownish grey spotted with brown.

The pouch is a strong leathery tissue with no feathers upon it.

I was much interested in seeing this bird and I am sorry that I have not written you about it before.

                              Good night,
                                  Chum.

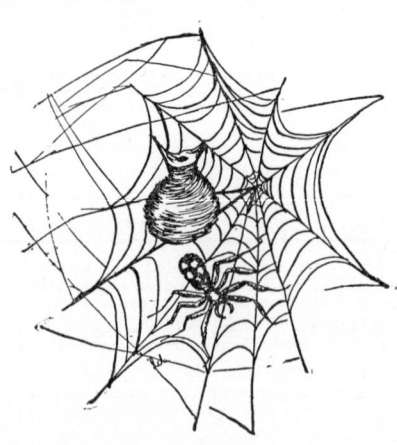

I TOLD DIAMOND, THE SHEPHERD DOG, "NOW THAT I HAVE SEEN THE SHEEP, I WILL TREAD MY BLANKET WITH MY BIG PAWS AND THANK THE WOOLY SHEEP FOR GIVING IT TO ME."

I LIFTED THE LATCH WITH MY BIG PAW

THE COW AND THE CALF

Dear Pussy Cousin:

We have gone to board on a farm. You know I have never seen a real farm before.

The cow here has a beautiful little calf. He has been taken away from his mother and put in a box stall. He cried for her and she mooed for him.

I overheard the farmer say that he wished the butcher would come for that calf. That made me feel dreadful, so I went into the barn to comfort the poor little fellow.

I said to the calf, "Do not tell on me and I will lift that latch with my big paw. When the door swings open, you go straight to your mother."

You would have laughed to have seen him run on his poor, little wobbly legs. I went up into the loft, where I could see and hear. The farmer came and found the calf with his mother.

Putting him back in the stall, he said, "No one has passed me to let that calf out. Perhaps I did not latch the door."

As soon as he was well out of the way, I pulled the latch again. Out ran the calf. We tried that performance four times that day. The last time, the farmer looked at the little fellow with his mother and said, "If you are smart enough to lift that latch and get out, I will not sell you to the butcher, but will raise you."

You see, after all, the farmer had a kind heart.

I cannot look him in the face, but I feel that I have done a good deed, even if it was through a trick.

I am going to bed feeling very happy and not one bit ashamed of myself.

            Good night,
              Chum.

JIMMY SPIDER

Dear Pussy Cousin:

My mistress would not let me go riding with her today. It made me cross and sulky. I went down on the porch to tell old Bob, the dog, my troubles. He was asleep, so I did not

WE WATCHED JIMMY SPIDER WEAVE HIS WEB

disturb him. I saw Millie and Jack going across the field. They are the boy and girl that live here on the farm. I started to run after them, but had only gone a few rods when I met Bill Grackle.

"Come with me, Chum, and see what you can do for a poor spider," said Bill. "He spun a wonderful web. It took him hours to do it, and moved his family in only this morning. Mrs. Spider was so happy with the beautiful swinging cradle that Mr. Spider made for the twins. Along came Jack beating the bushes with a stick, and swept the poor little spider's home completely away."

We found Mrs. Spider with the twins, crying, in the grass. Mr. Spider looked so discouraged. He did not have the heart to start weaving a new web. I told him to cheer up; that I would find him a much better place to build his home.

I took him to the fence corner and showed him how the morning sun would dry the dew from his web. He was very much pleased and started right in weaving a new home.

I told Billy Grackle to go back and get Mrs. Spider and the twins. They crawled on his back and he flew to the fence corner where we all watched Mr. Spider weaving his new home.

Did you ever see a spider weave his web?
If you once watch one you will never destroy it.

Good night,
Chum.

HOLD ON, IT WILL BE LIKE RIDING IN AN AEROPLANE

THE CADDICE FLY

Dear Pussy Cousin:

I went with my mistress and the children in the car two hundred and fifty miles from here to the state forest reserve. We drove up a winding road almost to the top of the mountain.

They parked the car and we walked along the edge of a swift little mountain stream. When we came to a large flat rock that hung over the stream, my mistress said, "We will stop here children, and sit on this rock to study the caddice worm. It lives in swift flowing streams just like this one."

I looked over the edge of the rock, down into the water.

"There is a caddice worm crawling along in its case," said my mistress.

"Why, I thought that was a pile of little stones," said Millie.

"The caddice worm spins a tube of silk around its body. It then fastens little pieces of sticks or stones to the tube with its strong silken web, cementing them together with a fluid which comes from its glands. It lives in this house and carries it around with it while it is a whitish larva," said my mistress.

"Watch it climb up that plant," said Jack.

It put out the front part of its body and slowly crawled up the stem of the plant, dragging its house behind it.

"There are a number of species of caddice flies," said my mistress. "Each one makes a different kind of a house. Some are carpenters and build their houses of little pieces of straw or sticks. This one that we are now watching is a mason, for it prefers to build its house of stone."

"There is one on that rock," said Millie. "Why look, it has used little snail shells."

"I often wonder how the baby snails like being dragged about in this manner by the caddice worm," said my mistress, "for the caddice worm, although it is burdened by this house on its back, moves very swiftly in the water."

"I bet they like it," said Jack. "It must be a new sensation for a snail to move quickly."

"Now I am going to show you what a wonderful fisherman the caddice worm is," said my mistress. "It wove that fish net of silk which comes from glands in its mouth."

"There is one between those two stones," said Jack. "It is funnel shaped, opening up stream. You see the water flows very rapidly here, keeping the net open."

"In the center of this net there are threads of silk, extending in two directions at right angles to each other,"

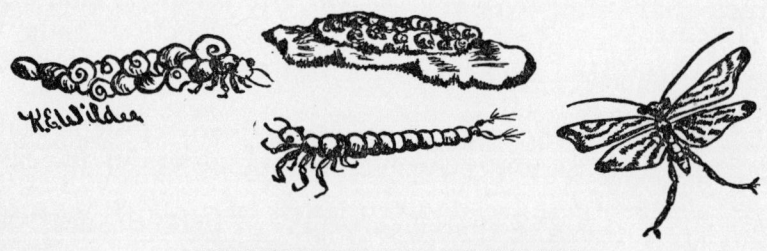

LIFE HISTORY OF THE CADDICE FLY
EGGS, LARVA, PUPA, AND CADDICE FLY

said my mistress. "This makes it look just like the meshes of a real net."

"When we go down to the falls, children," said my mistress, "we will find a great many of these little fish nets, all cast by these jolly little fishermen, whose silken web is so strong that the swift current does not tear it apart."

"That caddice worm on the rock has built a little door in the end of its house to keep all intruders out," said my mistress. "This door has an opening to allow the water to flow in and out so that the pupa can breathe. Sometimes the caddice worm builds a grating of silk instead of a door over the entrance."

While we were looking, one of the caddice worms came out of its house and swam to the top of the water near a rock that was just above the surface. It used its long middle legs to swim with.

My mistress focused her spy glass upon this caddice worm. Its wings looked like pads. A little ripple washed the insect up on this rock, out of the water. In an instant its wings were fully expanded and it flew away before the next ripple washed up over the rock.

"Lucky for it that it did not take as long as the dragon fly to expand and dry its wings," said Jack, "for if it had it would have been washed back into the water and destroyed."

Millie was so excited that she hopped up and down on the rock, saying, "Come back, come back. We want to see what you look like."

"Be quiet and sit down, Millie," said my mistress. "It will never come back if you hop up and down like that and frighten it."

We sat very still for a few minutes. Soon the caddice fly flew back to the dry rock near us.

"See children, the caddice fly looks like a moth," said my mistress. "It has four wings which are membranous and are covered with long scale-like hairs. When its wings are not in use, they are folded against the sides of the body in an almost vertical position, which makes the insect look very narrow and elongated. The hind wings are broader than the fore wings."

"The caddice flies are attracted by the light, just as the moths are," said my mistress.

The children enjoyed this trip very much. They went about identifying the different trees and woods plants.

There are many other interesting things that my mistress called the children's attention to. I will write you about them later.

Good night,
Chum.

THE SHARK'S EGG

Dear Pussy Cousin:

My mistress thinks that the most sensible fish in the sea is the shark, because it protects its eggs in a case. This case is very curious looking. It has a slit at both ends, which allows a free circulation of water through it. When a child my mistress called it the beetle of the sea, because it looked like the big horned beetle.

The mother shark is a wonderful fish mother, because she makes this cradle for her babies. It becomes attached to

SHARK'S EGG CASE

the seaweed and rocks back and forth in the sea. Nothing can disturb her babies in this little cradle. When the baby shark grows large enough it opens the cradle and comes out to swim around just like its parents.

My mistress drew a shark's egg case for the children. She said that it was shiny black, and was a hard shell when it was dry.

These shark's cases are frequently found on the beach. They have long strings, one on each of the four corners, that curl around pieces of seaweed which hold them in place until the little sharks are ready to swim out into the ocean.

I hope that I will find an empty shark's cradle on the beach next summer.

Good night,
Chum.

THE FRINGED GENTIAN

Dear Pussy Cousin:

I followed a butterfly to the fringed gentian. It lit on one of the blossoms and made a beautiful picture with its gorgeous coloring against the blue of the fringed gentian.

The butterflies look so happy as they flit from flower to flower, saying a jolly word to each little blossom as they take a sip of nectar.

"What is your name, Mr. Butterfly?" I asked.

"I am called the Tiger Swallow-tail and I belong to the Papillo family," it said.

It told me that the butterflies were message bearers for the flowers. That they carried the news of the flower world from plant to plant. That is why the flowers are glad to see them.

"The news that they are most interested in," said the butterfly, "is the color of the gowns that the flowers are wearing that came from seed this year. They never know what shade these flowers are going to be until they blossom, because the bees and butterflies carry the pollen from plant to plant, making all sorts of color combinations."

"So when I alight on a flower I whisper to it that the poppies are white, pink, yellow and red this year; that the seed of the pansy that wore a deep purple gown last year has just blossomed with purple petals splashed with yellow," said the butterfly.

"The little white pansy's seeds have blossomed with blotches of violet on their gown. The white pansy is very happy because its seedlings have some color instead of being pure white. It said that it had always coveted the violet gown of the pansy next to it, though it knew that this was not right," said the butterfly.

"So you see, Chum, the butterflies are very happy because they make others happy, by spreading the news of the plant world. In return the flowers give us nectar," said the Swallow-tail.

The butterfly bade me good-bye, and flew away to tell the whole countryside that the fringed gentians were in blossom.

"Do you know that your shade of blue is the fashionable color this year for women's gowns, and that fringe is in vogue, too?" I said to the fringed gentian.

THE SWALLOW TAIL BUTTERFLY
LIT ON THE FRINGED GENTIAN

"How lovely! I am right in style then," it said. "I would not have my name if I did not have my fringe. That is why I am called the fringed gentian. I grow so stiff and straight, that if it were not for my fringe, I would not be graceful at all."

"Why I think you are graceful," I said. "Your long slender buds are so dignified. You are not stiff at all."

"Thank you, Chum," it said. "I am very glad you think so. I do like the color of my dress, and the fringe is so different from the other plants. I do not want a dress like everyone."

When I bade it good-bye, the wind blew its petals back and forth, and its beautiful blue gown gleamed in the sunlight.

As I smiled back at it I could not help thinking how wonderful the plant life is on this earth.

Good night,

Chum.

THE TREE HOPPERS

Dear Pussy Cousin:

Bill Grackle and I were talking under a maple tree this morning. I looked up, and to my surprise the branch appeared to be covered with thorns. I rubbed my eyes with my big paw and looked again.

THE TREE HOPPERS RAISED UP ON THEIR LITTLE LEGS
AND LOOKED AT US

Bill began to laugh. "Thought you were seeing things, did you, Chum?" said Bill. "Those are not thorns, but tree hoppers. Look closely and you will see the jolliest faces into which you have ever looked."

The eyes of the tree hoppers were very droll looking. The line that separates the head from the body gives them the appearance of wearing glasses. While we were looking, one raised up on its little legs and hopped away. This hopping motion is the reason these insects are called tree

34

hoppers. The one which hopped away evidently told the others to look at us, for they all looked down and some flew away. Their wings had been folded under their hard shells.

Bill showed me several scars on the branch that had healed over. These were the egg pockets of the tree hoppers of last year. The female cuts a wide slit in the bark into which she inserts the eggs in clusters. They are arranged in two parallel rows. The slit is cut in such a way as to make the bark shrink back. This shrinkage forms a little cup that holds the eggs and stops the growth of the bark, thus preventing their being crushed by the growth of the twig.

To protect these eggs from the weather and from other insects, the tree hopper covers them with a foamy substance which hardens and makes a little house over them.

The young hatch in the spring. During their life they feed upon the sap of the tree by inserting their beaks through the tender bark and sucking the juice.

Some tree hoppers excrete honey dew, of which the ants are very fond. So you will always see ants around the tree hoppers.

You and Aunt Polly must look for these jolly little brownies on bushes and trees. They are also found on the bittersweet and the wood vine.

When you see a brown thorn where no thorn should be, you will find one of these little brownies cuddled close to a branch, with its legs drawn up so close to it that it appears to be a part of the tree.

Good night,
Chum.

TREE HOPPERS, EGGS, FOAM COVERING AND LAST YEAR'S EGG POCKET

SPICES

Dear Pussy Cousin:

We could not go out this morning because it was raining; so my mistress showed Millie how to make a spice cake.

I came into the kitchen, sat on a chair, and watched my mistress get out the flour and the eggs, the butter and the sugar. Then she said to Millie, "Now, Millie, no girl should make a cake until she knows all about the spices that she puts into it and how they grow, so I am going to take each spice and have you read about it."

"Jack, go wash your hands," said my mistress, "and then grate these nutmegs while Millie reads about the spices."

Millie began to read.

"Nutmegs are the dried kernels of the seeds of Myristica fragrans, a tree like the orange tree. The fruit resembles a small peach in size and shape. When ripe the fruits are gathered by hand. The seeds are dried in ovens, or in the sun, until the kernels rattle. The thick, fleshy outer covering, when dried, separates into two halves, exposing the true kernel or nutmeg. The nutmeg is then cleaned and packed for export.

"Cloves are the unopened flower buds of Caryophyllus aromatious, an evergreen tree that grows in Zanzibar and Pomba. The clove is the most important agricultural product of that section. The young flower buds are picked from August to November. The cloves are then spread in the sun to dry. The curing takes about a week. Cloves owe their valuable properties to the presence of a considerable quantity of oil of cloves."

Millie then turned to allspice in the book and read: "Allspice consists of the dried unripe fruits of Pimenta pimenta, a beautiful tree about thirty feet high. It is a native of Mexico, the West Indies, and South America. The fruits are round berries, of a dark purple color when ripe. They are picked by hand when green and are carefully cured. The name "allspice" is taken from the odor, which resembles a combination of the fragrance of cinnamon, cloves, and nutmegs."

"Cinnamon is next," said Millie. "This spice is the bark of the young shoots of Cinnamonum zeylanicum, a small evergreen tree of Ceylon. The bark is slit and removed in strips. It is then dried and contracts into "quills," which are tied into bundles. The finest qualities of cinnamon are yellowish-brown in color, smooth and thin. Inferior grades are darker and thicker. As in most species the fragrance is due to the presence in the bark of a volatile oil (oil of cinnamon)."

As Millie closed the book, she said, "Let us make some vanilla cookies, too."

"All right," said my mistress. "Who can tell me about vanilla?"

"I can," said Jack, "for I read all about the vanilla bean last night."

"Vanilla comes from the cured pods of the vanilla plant. It is a climbing plant found in Mexico and cultivated in the tropics," said Jack. "The vines are trained over small trees. When the vine blossoms, the flowers are pollinated by hand. The pods reach full size in about six weeks and turn yellow when ripe.

NUTMEG, CLOVES, ALLSPICE AND VANILLA BEAN

"Before the pods are ready for the market, as vanilla, they are cured. During this process the odor is developed. The flavor is due to the presence of a substance known as vanillin contained in a fluid which permeates the whole fruit," said Jack.

"The pods are placed in a basket and plunged into hot water several times. They are then put in boxes lined with a blanket to sweat, and covered to retain the heat. The pods turn a chocolate brown color. They are then placed on shelves and slowly dried to perfect the curing," said Jack.

"The extract of vanilla is made from these beans by the manufacturer," said Jack.

"It is fun to know how everything grows that you eat and wear. I never realized it before," said Millie.

"Oh, Millie," said my mistress, "do not bang the oven door so or your cake will fall."

"Yes," said Jack, "I bet you Chum could close that door better than that with his big paw."

I like the smell of vanilla. I had a piece of vanilla cooky and it tasted very good.

Aunt Polly and you are in the kitchen so much that I thought you would like to know about the spices.

I remember that Nora made spice cake.

                              Good night,
                                    Chum.

"HOW DO YOU MAKE THIS TRAP-DOOR?" I ASKED THE SPIDER

THE TRAP-DOOR SPIDER

Dear Pussy Cousin:

Can you imagine my surprise this morning while sitting on the grass to see a little door open out of the ground and a spider walk out.

"I am Jimmy Spider's friend," I said, "so do not be afraid of me. My name is Chum. What is your name?"

"I am called the trap-door spider," she said. "We build our nests under the ground very much as the miner wasps do and line the nest with our web, which makes it warm and soft for our babies when they hatch out. I lay my eggs in this warm little nest and make a door to cover it. The door is larger than the hole and rounded at the top so that it will shed the rain and keep the baby spiders nice and dry."

"But how do you make this trap-door?" I asked her.

"I weave my web back and forth and then put mud over it," said the spider. "I wet this mud with the fluid that comes from my glands. This acts as a cement that binds the web and mud together. I make layer after layer of this mud, reinforcing it with my web, just as people reinforce concrete, until I have formed the door. Then I weave hinges with my strong web so that the door will open and shut. The fluid that I use to mix the mud and web together makes it waterproof."

"When the eggs hatch, do your spider babies open the door and come out into the world?" I asked.

"Yes," said the spider.

I then told her about Jimmy Spider and the twins. She said that she would like to go with me sometime to visit them.

If you see a little door open in the earth in front of you, you will know that it is a trap-door spider's home.

Love to you and Aunt Polly.

Good night,
Chum.

THE CLOVER

Dear Pussy Cousin:

This morning I took a walk up the hill to look at the clover plant that I had admired the other day. Mr. and

THE ROOTS WERE COVERED WITH CURIOUS LITTLE KNOBS

Mrs. Clover looked very sad, while Grandma and Grandpa Clover had their heads drooping in deepest sorrow. I asked them what had happened.

Grandma Clover said that the seeds that she had so carefully sown last year had all come up and that the whole Clover family had increased three-fold. A girl just came along, pulled the biggest plant up by its roots, and then left it lying in the hot sun to wither and die.

Grandpa Clover said that he did not mind having the blossoms picked. It makes flowers very happy to be put into a vase of water to make the home beautiful or to cheer the sick. But it is very wicked for boys and girls to pick flowers and then throw them away or to pull off the flowers' heads so they cannot go to seed and make more beautiful flowers for next year.

I found the clover plant that had been pulled up by the roots and dug a hole with my big paws. As I was spreading out the roots in the hole I noticed that they were full of funny little knobs and asked Grandpa Clover what they were.

He held up his head proudly and told me that they were nitrogen. I then asked him what nitrogen was.

"Nitrogen is a chemical taken from the air by the clover plant," said Grandpa Clover. "It forms little nodules or swellings on the roots. Each nodule is a house full of living bacteria. These give the nitrogen which is a valuable fertilizer to the soil. If the clover plants are picked and the roots allowed to remain in the ground the full benefit of the nitrogen is saved."

This is very interesting, I thought, as I carefully spread out the roots of the poor clover plant so that each little rootlet could find plenty of food and moisture. I then covered them all very carefully with rich brown earth, pressing it down firmly all around with my big paws.

When I stop to think of all the wonderful things I see every day to write about I feel very sorry for the boy or girl who cannot see that each insect, bird, and plant has its individual life, which means much to Mother Earth. Their lives are as much a part of this old world as are the lives of the children.

Good night,
Chum.

THE BALTIMORE ORIOLE

Dear Pussy Cousin:

My mistress said to the children this morning, "I have a secret that I am going to share with you today. A Baltimore oriole has brought his bride to the big elm tree in front of the house. You can see them building their nest from my window. You must be very quiet and not disturb them. I had Mary get me some grocer's twine yesterday.

THE BALTIMORE ORIOLES WOVE THE STRING IN AND OUT TO FORM THEIR NEST

I threw it into a branch of the tree and put some hay on the ground. I looked out of my window this morning and found that the orioles had appreciated my donation, for they were busy weaving the string into their nest."

I lay on the porch and covered my face with my big paws so that the orioles would think that I was asleep, while the folks were watching them from the window upstairs.

Mr. Oriole took a piece of string and flew around the branch with it and then dropped it down. Mrs. Oriole took the end of the string and flew up to a branch and passed the string around it. She then drew it through in a slip knot with her bill, tied it, and dropped the end again.

Mr. Oriole flew down, took the end and fastened it to another branch. Then he flew to where my mistress had hung the string. He pulled out another piece and went with it to the new nest. He fastened it, dropped it, picked it up and twisted it around a branch and wove it in and out of the nest.

The orioles formed a hammock or cradle of the string, which made the foundation for their nest. They then brought some pieces of dried grass and wove them back and forth and in and out of the string.

They made the nest much larger at the bottom than at the top. It was very deep and strong. When they finished, they both perched on a nearby branch and surveyed the nest. Mr. Oriole then flew away and was gone quite a while. Back he came with some pieces of wild cotton with which they lined the nest.

My mistress told the children that she had a friend who had two orioles that had lost their mother and that she had brought them up. She kept them in a cage until they were big birds and then one day she opened the door of the cage and let them out. They flew around happily and when night came, back they went into the cage.

Instead of flying away with the other birds, they stayed in the cage and were quite happy in her conservatory all winter.

When spring came, out they flew and for several years they were her pets. They attracted a number of other orioles so that she called her country home the "Orioles Nest".

The Baltimore Oriole is a little larger than a sparrow.

The male is reddish orange on the lower back and under parts; the head, neck, and front part of the back are black. The wings are black, white, and orange.

The female is dull orange below, yellowish olive and dusky above.

These birds are easily distinguished by their unusual coloring.

My mistress told the children that all birds respond to kindness and that any boy or girl can make pets of the birds if they are kind to them and feed them.

I shall ask Bill Grackle to introduce me to the orioles, because probably they are prejudiced against cats, as all birds are. Good night, Chum.

THE PAPER WASPS

Dear Pussy Cousin:

The monarch butterfly told me that the wind had blown down the big wasp's nest, where the yellow jackets had lived for so long.

THE BIG NEST OF THE PAPER WASP

I went over to see what I could do for them.

When I arrived, the nest was tied to another branch with a piece of string. The butterfly, the bee, and the wasps were on the branches looking at the nest.

"A good joke on me," said the butterfly. "When I flew past here yesterday morning, the nest was on the ground."

Later Jack came along, took the nest, crawled out on the branch, and tied it firmly in place. The wasps made two or three new layers around the bottom where it was broken and said, "It is a much better place. It is braced from the strong north wind by the branch, which helps to support its weight."

I asked the wasp how the nest was made.

The bee was so amused that it stood on its head and said, "Oh, Chum, what a question. You have been in the country all the time and don't know how a paper wasp makes its nest."

The wasp flew down beside me and told me how it made its nest.

"Did you not know, Chum, that we taught man how to make paper?" asked the wasp.

It then told me that many years ago a man lay on the ground watching some wasps. He saw them go to a fence, bite out a piece of wood, and chew, and chew, and chew it. Then they used this material to build their nest. Later the man examined their nest, and found it was made of wood fibers. He took a layer of the nest and wrote upon it.

The principle of making paper from wood is the same as that the wasps use in making their nest. Wood is ground to a pulp, and boiled until it becomes a sticky mass. It is then put under rollers, and pressed into sheets. The sheets are finished with a starchy substance, which gives them a smooth, glossy surface.

Paper is made waterproof by treating it with a preparation of paraffine or tar.

Most of the paper, today, is made from wood pulp, though it is not quite as strong as the paper made from rags.

"It has always made me very proud," said the wasp, "to think that we were the first papermakers in the country."

The wasp taught man to make paper from wood and if we watch more closely the life all about us, nature can teach us much that we should know.

          Good night,
           Chum.

THE FROG, THE HOP TOAD, AND THE TREE TOAD

Dear Pussy Cousin:

The frog called a meeting with the hop toad and the tree toad, to discuss the mosquito situation.

The boys have been killing the frogs with their air rifles and sling shots.

The farmer said last night that something must be done about the mosquitoes. If we do not kill them, we will have no summer people in town next year. We might put oil on the pond. This would kill the larvae of the mosquitoes that live there.

My mistress said, "Oil will also kill all the plant and animal life in the pond. They are what makes the country so attractive to city people. Do you think that the beautiful pond lilies could live or the dear old frogs sing so happily if we put oil on the water? To me, they are the most attractive part of the country."

"If we get the boys of the town together, and ask them not to kill the frogs, we will do much more good than by pouring oil on the pond. The frogs eat the young of the mosquitoes in the pond, as well as those flying around in the air. So do the hop toads and the tree toads," said my mistress.

"Have you noticed how they run out their hinged tongues and snap up a mosquito? The frog will sit very quietly as if it were asleep. A mosquito comes buzzing along. Suddenly, out darts the tongue of the frog, who a minute ago looked so sleepy. The mosquito is swallowed before it knows what has happened. Hundreds of mosquitoes and gnats are disposed of in this way," said my mistress.

"Jack, you and I will do something for this community," said my mistress. "Get your crowd of boys together and tell them what I have told you. There are hundreds of frog's eggs down in the shady end of the pond. They will soon hatch if they are let alone. You can see the little tadpoles moving about in the eggs now. I watched them yesterday

THE FROG, THE TREE TOAD AND THE HOP TOAD

getting ready to come out. Those little tadpoles will soon help catch the mosquitoes. Then the pond will be stocked with frogs, which will eat the larvae of the mosquitoes, so that next year we will have very few of them. So do not pour oil on the pond, but let the frogs do the work."

When I told the frog what my mistress said, it looked down at the toad, saying, "Mr. Toad, I do not think that we have been on our job. Let us form an anti-mosquito society. You toads and tree toads join us frogs in clearing this town of mosquitoes. Instead of going up to the garden, keep around the border of the pond, and you, Mr. Tree Toad, stay on the trees that hang over it and watch for stray mosquitoes. Between us all, we will show the people the real good that we can do for this community. Then they will respect the frog and not kill it."

When they were all together I could see how different they were. The frog told me that the hop toad's eggs were the long snaky coils that I examined when we visited the other end of the pond. The frog was estimating how many tadpoles there would be.

The frog was so pleased when I told him how my mistress enjoyed hearing them all sing.

My mistress told the boarding house keepers who were complaining about the pond breeding mosquitoes, that they did their share toward increasing this pest, by throwing tin cans out on dumps, where they became filled with water, and made a fine breeding place for the mosquitoes. If they would take their can opener and jab a little hole in the bottom of the can all of the water would drain out.

Good night,
Chum.

FROG'S EGGS, TADPOLES, TOAD'S EGGS AND YOUNG FROG

MRS. MEADOW MOUSE AND HER HOME

Dear Pussy Cousin:

It is clean-up week. Everyone is going around their place picking up all of the rubbish.

Mrs Grunt is so happy, for her pig pen has been whitewashed inside and out.

The chicken coop has also been whitewashed. Everything looks spick and span.

Millie told my mistress that the children cleaned up the school grounds yesterday. They are going to try not to allow any papers to lie about. They also dug up around the shrubbery.

Millie and Jack are going around the place with a wheelbarrow, picking up any trash that they can find.

I have been worried for fear that they would find the tin can that little Mrs. Meadow Mouse has taken for her home. You remember she was the mouse whose nest I dragged up to old Bob's dog kennel.

This year she has been very sensible. She took a tin can and made her nest inside of it. It made such a cunning little house.

This morning I went down to visit her. She looked up at me and said, "Chum, I have been so worried for fear that they would take my home, for this is cleanup week. Of course it is not very nice to have tin cans around the place."

"Don't worry, Mrs. Meadow Mouse," I said. "I have come here this morning to cover it up with my big paw."

"So you are going to help me out of my troubles once again," she said. "How can you do it, Chum?"

"It will be very easy for me. That pile of dead grass over there will be just the thing," I said. "I can drag it with my big paw and cover the tin can all up so no one will find it."

I dragged the grass up over her house. I peeked in and there were five little mouse babies. They were tucked away in the back part of the tin can, in the softest bed, made of grass and old pieces of rags.

"I have never had such a wonderful house, Chum. It keeps the rain from my babies and the cover on the tin can is an awning over my porch. It keeps the sun out of my babies' eyes and gives them plenty of air," said the mouse.

I was so busy dragging the grass up over the tin can with my big paw that I did not see my mistress and the children coming.

Mrs. Meadow Mouse gave a little squeal and ran into

LITTLE MRS. MEADOW MOUSE CAME OUT OF HER HOUSE

the tin can. I turned around and there was my mistress. "Why, Chum," she said, "what are you doing?"

"I have been watching him for quite a while before we got here," said Millie. "He seems to be dragging dead grass and putting it in that pile."

They all went over to the pile of grass and discovered the can.

Millie exclaimed, "Why, look at the darling little mouse and her babies."

"How cunning for her to use the tin can for her home," said my mistress.

Out ran Mrs. Mouse and hid in the grass.

"The poor little thing," said my mistress. "She thinks that because it is cleanup week we are going to take away her home. You need not worry, for we will not disturb you. We are going to help Chum cover it up, Mrs. Mouse."

"I believe that was just what he was doing; helping her conceal her nest," said Millie.

My mistress sat down beside me, lifted me up in her arms, and gave me a big hug.

"Chummy boy," she said, "was there ever such a kind hearted pussy in all the wide world? We are going to leave you to finish your job because little Mrs. Meadow Mouse does not seem to be a bit afraid of you. I bet that you and she have met before and are quite chummy."

After they went away little Mrs. Meadow Mouse came back and said, "Chum, this world would be a wonderful place if every girl and boy were as kind hearted as Millie and Jack, and thought of caring for the little animals as they do. They get much more out of life than the child who goes through the world with the idea that God places all the little creatures on this earth to be tormented and teased or destroyed. But Millie and Jack want everything that has been created to live and be happy."

Millie came back and put a piece of cheese and some crumbs of bread near Mrs. Meadow Mouse's house. Then she tiptoed away.

Mrs. Meadow Mouse came out of her little tin can house.

"What a feast, Chum," she said. "I wish that my babies were big enough to enjoy it with me."

Now the children are feeding little Mrs. Meadow Mouse every day. She has grown so tame that she comes out of her tin can house and sits in front of it, while they give her food.

Millie says that if ever a mouse smiled her thanks, she does.

Mrs. Meadow Mouse's babies are learning that the children are her friends and will soon come out and nibble their dinner, while the children sit quietly in the grass and watch them.

What a happy home the can is, for the mouse knows that it is being cared for by loving little hearts, who want to make everything that God has created happy in this world.

         Good night,
           Chum.

THE FAMILY CIRCLE

THE PRAYING MANTIS, THE WALKING STICK, THE KATYDID, MRS. GRASSHOPPER, THE LOCUST, MR. GRASSHOPPER, THE CRICKET AND THE LEAF INSECT FORMED A CIRCLE TO RECEIVE THE GUESTS AT THE FAMILY REUNION IN THE MEADOW.

THE FORMATION OF GRAIN IN WOOD

Dear Pussy Cousin:

My mistress said to Jack last night, "Here are some sections of wood that I found in a box yesterday, showing how a log, when cut at different angles, will produce a different looking grain.

"In woods grown in a climate where the season of growth is followed by a period of rest, when **tree growth is** at a standstill, the pores and fibers of which the wood is composed are larger and have thinner walls during the period of active growth than those formed at the end of the season, thus making a sharp line between the growth of one season and that of the next. These seasonal growth **layers are** called 'annual rings,'" said my mistress.

"This end of the log shows these annual rings very plainly," said my mistress. They look like circles on the log, cousin Ted. My mistress added that there was one ring for each year's growth and that one could tell how old a tree was by counting these rings.

Woods are made up of vertically elongated cells aggregated into strips running at right angles to the fiber from the bark toward the center. These are known as medullary rays.

"Because wood has annual rings and medullary rays, it can be cut longitudinally in two distinct ways: at right angles to the rays, producing plain sawed lumber; and parallel to the rays and across the rings, producing what is known as quarter sawed lumber," said my mistress.

Plain sawed lumber is usually cheaper than quarter sawed because it is cut with less waste. In some kinds of woods it has a better figure.

Quarter sawed lumber shrinks less in width and is not so likely to check or twist in drying."

"What is veneer?" asked Millie.

"A veneer is a thin sheet of wood. Several of these sheets are glued together or glued on thicker, cheaper lumber," said my mistress. "Veneer is either cut in straight sheets from a squared timber or peeled off in a continuous layer from a rotating log. Straight sheets are cut with a saw or a knife. They have the advantage that they can be cut in any direction. If cut radially they will produce the types of figure that is obtained by quarter sawing."

"When veneer is taken from a rotating log it can be produced cheaply and in large sheets, and its growth ring figure is continuous," said my mistress.

"Figure in wood is the pattern formed by irregular portions of coloring matter, by the annual rings and the medullary rays, and by cross grain, burls, or knots," said my mistress.

HOW THE GRAIN FORMS IN WOOD

"All woods have some figure, but in many species it is obscure or uninteresting. No two pieces of wood show the same figure," said my mistress.

"In lumber cut from crooked or bulged logs the figure assumes peculiar shapes. Some knots in wood are very decorative," said my mistress. "I will tell you some day about burl and curly maple."

"My dressing table is made of bird's-eye maple," said Millie.

"Yes, I will tell you about that, too," said my mistress.

I am anxious to hear more about wood grain and so are the children.

Good night,
Chum.

THE YEAST PLANT

Dear Pussy Cousin:

Mary could not make the bread because she was ill.

My mistress told her not to worry, that she wanted Millie to learn to make bread, so she would show her.

Millie took the tin foil off of the yeast cake. "Where does yeast come from?" she asked.

My mistress told her that yeast was an invisible little plant; that the yeast cake had millions of little yeast plants in it.

"The yeast plant is a colorless oval," said my mistress. "When it is full grown, a bud starts to grow from one side. Look at the yeast through the microscope. See those cells growing and forming little buds or new cells. They thrive on sugar. This changes into two other substances: alcohol and carbon dioxide gas."

"When preserves 'work,' it is because yeast plants are present," said my mistress.

"How does the yeast get in the preserves?" asked Millie.

"Yeast is floating in the air," answered my mistress. "It may fall upon food causing it to ferment and become sour. Yeast plants are killed by boiling."

"I think that wheat flour makes the best bread," said my mistress. "It contains starch and gluten. The starch turns into sugar to feed the yeast plants, and the gluten, which is elastic, holds the dough together and stretches as the bread rises. The yeast is growing in the bread. The sugar changes to alcohol and carbon dioxide. Both of these substances pass off in the baking. The carbon dioxide is a gas that expands as it is heated, causing the dough to become lighter."

"Yeast must have food, moisture, and warmth to grow," said my mistress. "It gets its food from the sugar, its moisture from the liquid in the bread, and its warmth from the heat of the room. The best temperature for growth is from 70 to 80 degrees."

"Is it the holes in the bread that make it light?" asked Millie.

"Yes, but the dough would not rise or have the little holes in it if it were not for the yeast," said my mistress.

"Do you suppose our bread will be just as good as Mary's?" asked Millie.

"I do not see why it will not be," answered my mistress.

"Tomorrow morning we will knead it, make it into loaves, and set them where it is warm, so that the dough will rise again," said my mistress.

"Why do you make it rise twice?" asked Millie.

"It makes the bread lighter and gives it a finer grain," answered my mistress, as she covered up the dishpan of dough with a towel and left Jingles and Snooky in the warm kitchen. Tabby insisted on sleeping in the attic.

Jingles and Snooky are to stay with us for a few days, while our neighbor next door is away. We are having a jolly time.

I will write you how the bread came out.

Good night,
Chum.

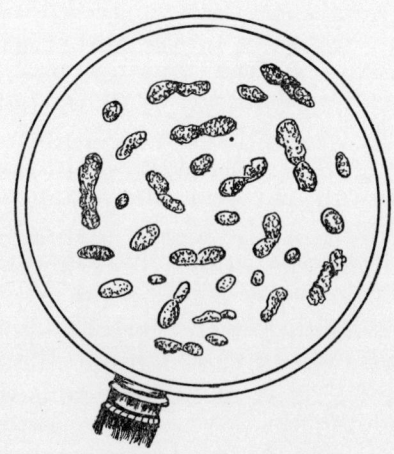

MAGNIFIED YEAST PLANTS

THE KITTENS AND THE BREAD

Dear Pussy Cousin:

What do you think happened to the bread?

When we came down in the morning, Jingles and Snooky were in the dish pan that the bread was set in. They had pulled off the cloth. Jingles said that he heard my mistress say that the bread would rise, so he thought that it would be great fun to get on top of it and be lifted up as it rose. So they both got into the pan to see how it would feel to have the bread lift them up. It took such a long time that they fell asleep.

When they woke up in the morning, they could not get out, for the dough had risen all over them.

Millie and my mistress were angry at the kittens spoiling the bread, but could not help laughing, for they were such a funny sight.

My mistress carried the pan of bread just as it was, with the cats in it, to Mary's bedside. "Glory be, what in the world were they thinking of?" said Mary.

"They thought it would make a nice soft bed," said my mistress. "Let us clean them all up before Tabby sees them, for she will be distressed." So my mistress lifted each of the kittens out of the dough and with screams of laughter, the children scraped the dough from the cats with a knife.

My mistress then put Snookums on the table and said, "Snookums, if I tell your mistress what you have done and what a disgrace you have been to her, she will never want to see you again. I am not going to tell her. If you do anything more that is naughty while you are visiting us, you will have to be shut up in the garage. We are not going to tell Tabby, your mother, either, so you must go to work and lick yourselves all off."

I helped them, but it was a very naughty thing for them to do. After they were cleaned, and my mistress had given the dough to Mrs. Grunt, Snooky came over to me and said, "Chum, it was very stupid of me to go to sleep and make all this fuss. I did not even have the fun of feeling myself rise with the bread. We played so hard with you last evening that we were tired out."

By the expression on his face I thought that he would like to try it again, so I said very severely, "Look here, Snooks, if you get into that fresh batch of bread to test out its rising qualities, something is going to happen to you."

He just giggled and scampered off.

My mistress kept the kittens out of the kitchen while she made a new batch of bread.

The rascals climbed up into the old lilac bush, looked in the kitchen window, and grinned at us all of the time the bread was being made.

They are the most mischievous kittens I have ever seen.

No one told their mother about it when she came down. I am glad, for she thinks that they have been very good kittens.

She is such an old dear herself that it would be too bad to worry her.

Good night,
Chum.

JINGLES AND SNOOKY IN THE BREAD DOUGH

PUSSY WILLOW TIME

HOW TO MAKE THIS PUSSY WILLOW CARD:
FIRST DRAW THE FENCE AND THE LEAVES,
THEN USE THE SEPALS FOR EARS,
THE PUSSY WILLOWS FOR THE HEAD, BODY AND TAIL

THE PANSY AND THE BEE

Dear Pussy Cousin:

Last summer I asked the bee, which was pollinating, to put some pollen from the brown pansy on the yellow one.

It only buzzed, so I thought it did not understand me. I started to lift it quite gently, with my big paw, from the brown pansy to the yellow one. It stung me on the paw and nose, so I went howling into the house. My mistress did my paw up and put mud on my nose. It got all over my whiskers.

She told me that was what people got when they interfered with other people's business. She said that the bee understands just how to carry the pollen from plant to plant and make the most wonderful color combinations. It goes to the flower to get the nectar, from which it makes the honey. In

THIS IS WHAT I GOT FOR INTERFERING WITH OTHER PEOPLE'S BUSINESS

so doing it covers its body and legs with pollen. It carries this from plant to plant, losing some of it in every flower it visits. Thus it makes the seeds which the next year grow to be beautiful flowers with new color combinations.

I was gratified when I went into the garden today to see the pansies. The big pansy looked up at me in her brown satin gown with ruffles of yellow, and if ever a pansy was proud of her gown, she was. I know jolly well that the bee would never have thought of that color scheme if I had not suggested it.

It was really nice when it flew past me today in the garden and just buzzed, "It does look well, it does look well."

There is so much to write about that will interest you and Aunt Polly that you will hear from me soon again.

Good night,

Chum.

AS THE BEE PASSED ME IN THE GARDEN IT BUZZED, "IT DOES LOOK WELL, IT DOES LOOK WELL"

THE SNAILS

Dear Pussy Cousin:

This morning I noticed three snails in the yard. I was interested in seeing how different they were. They were all land snails, two with shell houses and one without. They make their own little shell houses from a secretion of carbonate of lime.

They had long feelers, which were their eyes.

Did you ever see a snail's eye?

One of the snails told me that her eyes were not like mine. "You can only see straight ahead," she said. "We can look around the corner with our eyes."

"Where is your mother, Willie Snail?" she asked the little snail with the shell.

"She has gone to try to find this little fellow a house," he answered.

"Mercy me! your mother is always borrowing trouble, Willie Snail. Does she not know that that snail does not live in a shell and never had one? Did you, Freddie? He is called a slug," she said.

"It is nice for Willie Snail's mother to think of me," said Freddie. "I certainly appreciate it. I came up here to tell you snails that old Bob, the dog, has tipped over the garbage pail. I ate all that I could and came up to tell you about it."

"That is good of you. Where did you come from?" Willie Snail asked.

"I have lived around here for a long time, but I was a little afraid of you snails with those houses on your backs. Willie, I wish I had spoken to you before. You are quite a nice fellow. I think it was lovely of your mother to try to find me a house. Don't you, Mrs. Snail?"

"Yes, I suppose so. But one should always find out what another person needs before trying to get it for him. I am much obliged for your invitation to visit the garbage pail, but I have had my breakfast. Willie looks hungry; perhaps he will go."

I followed Willie Snail and his friend to the bucket, and was much amused to see the little fellow start his second meal and eat nearly twice as much as Willie.

When they saw the farmer coming they looked around the corner of the pail and hurried away. I see now what Mrs. Snail meant when she said that snails' eyes are long, so that they can see around a corner.

A most interesting thing is the slimy road track which snails lay as they go along. The flat surface on which the snail moves is called the stomach foot. The movement is like a wave. Having no feet, they draw their body through a slimy substance which is secreted from their slime glands. It makes them slide along easily, on a track of their own laying.

I asked Freddie Snail how he protected himself from the storms.

"I crawl under a board or a stone and am very comfortable. Between you and me, Mr. Chum, I prefer not to have a house to carry around with me. But don't tell Willie Snail, for he is proud of his shell."

I wonder if all the boys and girls who go into the country see all these wonderful things that are going on about them. Every animal, bird and insect has its individual life and way of living. Even the plants have their individuality. They are doing their work on this earth, just as the children are going to do their work when they grow up.

Good night,
Chum.

THEIR EYES LOOKED LIKE HORNS ON THEIR HEADS

THE BRONZE GRACKLE

Dear Pussy Cousin:

I met Bill Grackle this morning. "Billy," I said, "I get so indignant at people calling bronze grackles, blackbirds. Why is it? You don't look like a blackbird."

"We belong to the blackbird family," answered Billy.

"Well, you don't look, act, or talk like them; for they are black, while you are green and bronze, and make a noise like a rusty hinge."

How he did laugh, Cousin Ted.

"Chum," said Billy, "I don't believe that you know much about the bronze grackle, although we have been pals for so long."

I will tell you what Millie read from her note book last night about the bronze grackle, I said.

"You have metallic tints that are rich, deep, and uniform. Your head and neck all round are rich, silky steel blue. Prussian blue to brassy greenish is most apparent on your neck. Your entire body, above and below, is of a uniform continuous metallic brassy olive, varying to burnished golden olive bronze; with metallic purplish or reddish violet on the wings and tail.

"The iris is yellow, the bill, legs, feet and claws are black."

"Why, that sounds as though I am quite a respectable looking fellow," said Billy Grackle.

"We are widely distributed throughout the country and are a very social bird," said Bill. "We prefer to live in communities. We enjoy the company of people." Then with a grin Bill said, "and I like to chum it with a cat."

"We are very beneficial, for we eat many caterpillars and insects," said Bill.

"You will find our nests in orchards or shade trees, near dwellings," said Bill. "We saddle our nest between two horizontal limbs or in forks of trees. It is a large and rather compact structure composed of coarse grasses, weeds, blades of corn or most any handy material, plastered together with mud and lined with fine grasses or rootlets."

"My mother laid four eggs, but some grackles lay six. The eggs are laid about the middle of April and are light greenish white, irregularly spotted, and marked with zigzag lines of rusty brown," said Bill.

"I told you that I belonged to the blackbird family. My relatives are the bobolink, the cowbird, the red-winged blackbird, the meadow lark, the orchard oriole, the Baltimore oriole, the rusty blackbird, Brewer's blackbird and the yellow-headed blackbird," said Bill.

I did not realize that Billy Grackle was related to all of these birds. Did you?

Good night,
Chum.

BILLY GRACKLE ON THE LECTURE STAND

THE ROBINS

Dear Pussy Cousin:

You remember Mr. and Mrs. Robin Red Breast. Their son Jim brought home his bride. They decided to build their nest under the eaves of the house, near my window. Jim told his bride that they had better build it in the corner, so that they would have the overhang of the roof to keep it dry and could use the return for a front porch.

Jimmy Robin brought a few sticks and some hay. It was interesting to see him brace a stick in the corner for a support. With Mrs. Robin's help he made a wonderful nest. Then he went to the hen yard, brought back a piece of down, and put it in the bottom of the nest, making several trips until the nest was lined with soft little feathers.

When I looked into the nest today, mother robin was feeding the three little robins a worm that Jim Robin had brought her. He is a most devoted husband and father. He keeps Mrs. Robin supplied with worms for herself and the children. Before the little robins were hatched, he sat on the nest while Mrs. Robin went for a drink of water, stretched her wings, and obtained the exercise she needed.

Mr. Robin's mother called and brought the children a big fat grub. Young Mrs. Robin did not want the children to have the grub, as she feared it would make them sick. Grandma Robin was very angry. "Just as though I had not brought up dozens of little robins," she said. "This new way of feeding according to rule can be carried too far. This grub will make them fat and lively."

Young Mrs. Robin asked Jimmy Robin what he thought. He said that Grandma Robin fed him and he was the strongest robin on the farm. So the little robins ate the grub, and Grandma Robin went away well pleased.

It is interesting to see the difference in those three little robins. Betty Robin is so helpful to her mother. She picks all of the down in the nest with her little bill and makes up the bed all fresh every morning.

MR. ROBIN THREW LAZY PETE OUT OF THE NEST

Willie Robin and she were the first to fly, but lazy Pete hardly gets out of the nest. He makes his father and mother wait on him, bringing him food and water. He never tries to exert himself or to help his parents in any way.

His mother told him that his sister and brother were at the head of the class in the bird school. She met Bill Grackle this morning and he told her how smart and self-reliant her two robins were.

"Peter, we are not going to bring you any more worms," said his parents. "You will have nothing to eat unless you fly with us to the plowed field. Your brother and sister are there now getting their breakfast."

"But you told us, father, that we steered with our tails, and I have no tail yet to steer with, so how can I fly?" asked Pete.

Mr. and Mrs. Robin flew away. Pete pouted all day long. When Mr. and Mrs. Robin came back they had nothing for him. Mr. Robin asked him if he was hungry.

"Yes. Go get me something to eat," he said.

"No, I do not intend to get you anything to eat," said his father. "You are a big, strong bird, and you must take up your duties in the world, and make something of yourself. You cannot always depend upon your father and mother to take care of you."

Pete hung his head but made no effort to fly.

Suddenly Mr. Robin caught Pete by the back of the neck and threw him out of the nest. When Pete felt himself falling, he tried his wings and found that he could fly.

Mr. Robin looked up at me and said, "Sometimes we have to punish our children. They think that we are unkind to them. Pete would never have learned to fly if I had not dropped him out of the nest."

Pete is now going to the bird school, and wishes that he had started earlier, because he is behind all of the other robins of his age.

Good night,
Chum.

MOLD

Dear Pussy Cousin:

My mistress sent Millie down to the cellar to get some jelly for lunch. When she brought it up it was moldy.

"Gracious," said Millie, "look at the mold on top of this jelly."

"Yes," said my mistress, "go get Jack, and I will tell you children how mold forms and grows."

My mistress took the mold off of the jelly and placed it on a slice of damp bread. They all looked at the mold through a magnifying glass. She then put the bread where it was warm, to make the mold grow.

"Mold is a plant, like the yeast, but you can see it," said my mistress. "One mold plant sometimes spreads so that it covers a large space. Mold is not a green plant, so that it cannot make its own food."

"The growing part of a mold plant consists of a network of tiny threads, that look like a cobweb. The mold forces these threads between the particles of bread, fruit, jelly, etc., and obtains its food from them," said my mistress.

"A little ball grows up from this network. Later it opens and scatters its spore-like seed to the wind. These float around in the dust of the air, until they settle on some substance from which they may get their food. Each one of these tiny spores may start a new mold plant," said my mistress.

"You remember, children, that the yeast plant had to have food, moisture, and warmth, in order to grow," said my mistress. "Mold grows in the same way, but thrives best in still air. Mold will not grow where there is a good circulation of air, or where food is kept dry. That is why we should have our bread boxes ventilated."

"A whole barrel or basket of fruit may become moldy from one, as the mold spores will scatter over the rest of the fruit," said my mistress. "Jelly is covered with paraffine to keep it from molding. If the mold spore falls on a **dry** surface it can do no harm. Mary did not cover this glass of jelly properly."

"I suppose that it is very wicked, but I am glad that the jelly was moldy, because I have learned so much," said Millie. "It is wonderful to know all about these things."

Good night,
Chum.

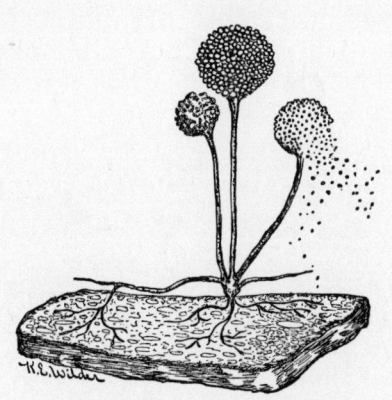

MAGNIFIED MOLD PLANT
GROWING ON A SLICE OF BREAD

GALL HOUSES

Dear Pussy Cousin:

    My mistress and the children were sitting under an oak tree, resting from a long hike. I spied a peculiar looking growth attached to a branch of the tree. I climbed up to look at it and touched it with my big paw, breaking off the branch, which had two of these curious looking balls growing on it.

    The branch dropped down beside my mistress. Looking up at me she said, "You rascal, I was just wondering what we would study this afternoon. Thank you, Chummy, for giving me this wonderful specimen of oak gall."

    "How curious it looks," said Millie.

    "Yes, it is the home of the oak gall fly or mite," said my mistress. "This little mite pierces the branch and lays an egg in the hole she has made. This causes the cells of the branch to swell and form a growth around the wound. The egg hatches and the tiny worm eats the inside of this house until it is large enough to emerge, when it appears as a little mite or four-winged fly, to take up its life work in the world about us."

    "Each species of the gall fly selects a different kind of plant, tree, or shrub and builds a home after its own architectural plan," said my mistress. "You have often seen a peculiar growth on the moss rose bush, like a round hairy ball. It is the home of that particular kind of gall fly. This moss rose gall is compound. I have always called it the gall flies apartment house, for it is a community containing many larvae, each in its own apartment."

    "We must find a gall apple on an oak tree," said my mistress. "The architect of this house has taken the shape of the apple for its home."

    "I have often noticed that round growth on the oak," said Jack. "I have one home in my collection. It has a hole in the side where the gall fly came out."

    "Jack, go over there in the field and see if you can find

a stalk of golden rod with a round warty swelling on it," said my mistress. "It is formed by the gall fly that selects the golden rod for its home."

Jack came back in a few minutes with a stalk of golden rod with a gall house upon it.

"The life history of each species of gall mite or gall fly is worth studying," said my mistress. "Let us make this oak gall a start for our collection of galls."

"I am going to hug Chum for giving us our first specimen," said Millie.

I like to be petted but I don't like to be hugged.

Good night,
Chum.

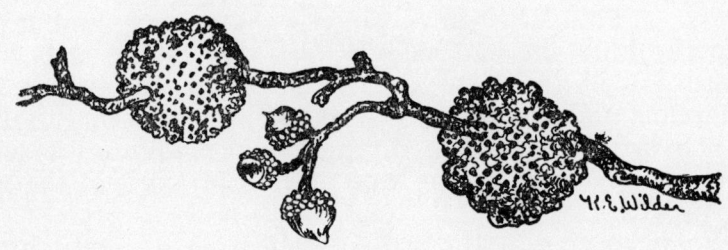

OAK GALL MADE BY THE GALL FLY

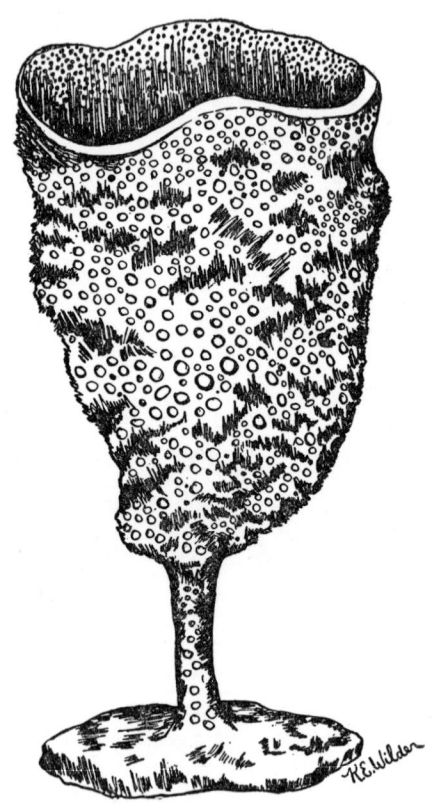

THE CUP SPONGE

THE CUP SPONGE

Dear Pussy Cousin:

A friend of my mistress sent her a box of wonderful sea specimens from Bermuda. I will write you about them one at a time.

I have never seen anything so curious as the large goblet that my mistress lifted out of the box.

"Look children!" she exclaimed. "See what Professor Clark has sent me. A cup sponge. I have always wanted one."

"A cup!" said Millie, "It looks more like a goblet to me."

"Yes," said my mistress, "when I was a child, I thought that it was the goblet that Father Neptune drank out of. You know Father Neptune is the God of the sea. When you study mythology, Jack, you will learn all about him. He was a very wonderful old fellow."

"Let us not call it a cup sponge, but Neptune's goblet," said Millie.

My mistress then told the children how the sponge grows on a stem at the bottom of the ocean and how many different species there are.

She laughed as she patted my head and said, "Chum knows what a sponge is, for when we travel in the summer he has a velvet sponge. I put it in cold water and bathe his face and his big paws to cool him off."

"The velvet sponge," said my mistress, "has the finest texture of any of the commercial sponges."

"Sponges have been used since ancient times. The bath sponges being mentioned in both the Iliad and the Odyssey shows that they were used in the days of Homer. Scientists could not decide whether sponges were plants or animals until 1825. The sponges were then admitted to their rightful place in the animal kingdom," said my mistress.

"Sponges live in salt water, there being only one family among them all that lives in fresh water. They are widely distributed, being found on the rocks and in pools near the shore, down to great depths in the ocean.

"Their colors are very brilliant, being pink, lilac, red, yellow, and orange.

"Living sponges have an unpleasant odor which makes them safe from the attacks of sea animals. The crabs have taken advantage of this by planting bits of living sponge upon their limbs or bodies, where the sponge continues to grow. The odor of the sponge protects the crab from its enemies.

"A constant circulation of water is maintained by the sponge through its numerous tubes, from which minute particles of organic matter and microscopic organisms are extracted from the water, which forms the food supply of the sponge. The outgoing current carries away the rejected matter.

"The sponge, as we know it, is really the skeleton or supporting frame of the animal. It occurs as a system of skeleton fibers or as an elastic and felt-like tissue as we see it in the common bath sponge.

"The sponge passes its whole life attached to some object. Sometimes the base is drawn out to form a stalk, so the body of the sponge is raised above the bottom of the sea, as it is in this sponge.

"Sponges which grow on the floor of the ocean have a root tuft which serves as an anchor.

"This cup sponge is very beautiful. It looks like an old Egyptian vase," said my mistress.

There are many other interesting things in the box about which I am going to write to you.

                                Good night,
                                      Chum.

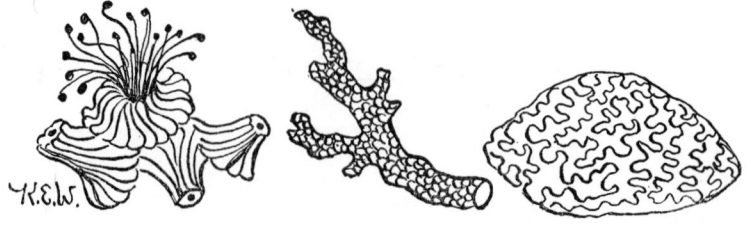

CORAL POLYPS, BRANCH CORAL AND BRAIN CORAL

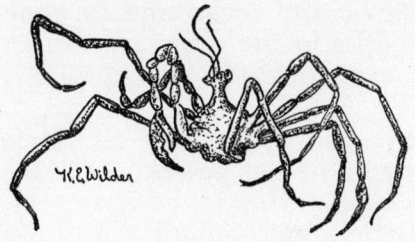
THE SPIDER CRAB

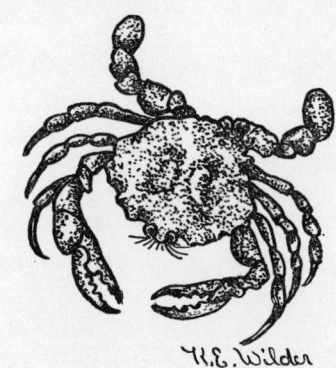
THE LADY CRAB

THE SHRIMP

THE SEA FAN

THE SEA FAN

Dear Pussy Cousin:

"How beautiful!" every one in the room exclaimed, when my mistress took a sea fan out of the box that Professor Clark sent from Bermuda.

"Can you imagine how wonderful the bottom of the ocean must look, with these growing there?" said my mistress. "This one was pink when it was growing. There are some that are a brilliant orange, while others are a deep coral pink."

"One can see these fans growing in the ocean by looking down through the glass bottoms of the boats that they have in Bermuda," said my mistress. "The water is as clear as crystal and you can see the plants in the water garden at the bottom of the ocean. It is a sight that no one will ever forget."

"What makes this sea fan so stiff?" asked Millie.

"Lime is formed on the sea fan from deposits of the little polyps or coral forming animals," said my mistress. "Some day I will tell you how coral islands are formed and all about my trip to them."

"The sea fans grow on coral reefs or rocks at the bottom of the ocean. They take beautiful and weird forms. The veins of the fans are the lime deposits of the little polyps or coral animals. The fans are not hard when the animals are alive, with their soft tentacles which move in the water. Only the lacy framework is left when the animals die and the fan is dried."

"There is another variety called the Ostrich Plume Sea Fan, which is beautiful when alive but when dry looks rather stiff," said my mistress.

"I shall write the professor and tell him what happiness his gifts have given us all," said my mistress. "This was surely a box of surprises."

Good night,
Chum.

THE MUD WASP

Dear Pussy Cousin:

How you would have laughed, if you could have seen the mud wasps stand on their heads this morning.

I watched them for quite a while, but did not know what they were doing, so I asked one of the wasps.

It flew up on the dead tree where I was sitting and told me that they were biting out pieces of clay to make their nests, although they looked as though they were standing on their heads.

"We always select a moist spot where there is clay," said the wasp. "These little balls of clay are used to build our nest. We use our tongues as trowels to form the cells of the nest."

I followed the wasp to the barn and went up in the loft where it was building.

Cousin Ted, you have no idea how interesting it was to watch them. The wasp brought a little ball of clay and smoothed it out with her tongue until it formed a part of one of the cells. Then she went back to the clay bank for more. It took many, many trips to build one little cell of the nest.

While she was gone I crawled out on the beam where she was building to get a good view of the new nest. The cells looked like little tubes.

When one cell was finished the wasp flew away. Back she came with an insect. She put it in the cell, laid an egg, and sealed up the cell.

I was curious to see what she would do next. She flew away and soon came back with more wet clay and started to build another cell next to the one that she had just sealed.

I have watched her for two or three days. Now she has five cells, all built and sealed, with an insect and an egg in each.

78

She told me that when the egg hatched, the baby wasp, or larva, as it is called, would eat the insect that was put in the cell before it was sealed up. Later it would bite its way out as a wasp.

"Do you always build your nest in barns or under the eaves of houses?" I asked.

THE MUD WASPS STOOD ON THEIR HEADS TO BITE OUT THE CLAY FOR THE CELLS OF THEIR NEST

"Yes, we do," said the wasp. "Our cousins the Vespa wasps make a round nest and build it on the branch of a tree or an old rail fence. They use mud, too."

"I never realized before how beautiful and lacy your wings are," I said. "Your jaws must be as strong as those of the carpenter ants."

"They are, Chum," she answered. "We, too, have a branch of our family that builds its nests in wood. I will show you one of these nests sometime."

"We are proud of our beautiful slender waists. We do not like the large waists that are in vogue now," said the wasp.

As I came out of the barn, another wasp was building a nest under the eaves.

"Do you go to sleep in the fall and then wake up in the spring?" I asked.

"Yes," answered the wasp. "We wake up in the spring, build our nest and lay our eggs so that the wasp family will increase."

"Why, Chum, where have you been all the morning?" asked my mistress. "I have called and called you."

I could not go with the wasp to see her cousins, the wood borers, but will go later and write you about them.

Good night,

Chum.

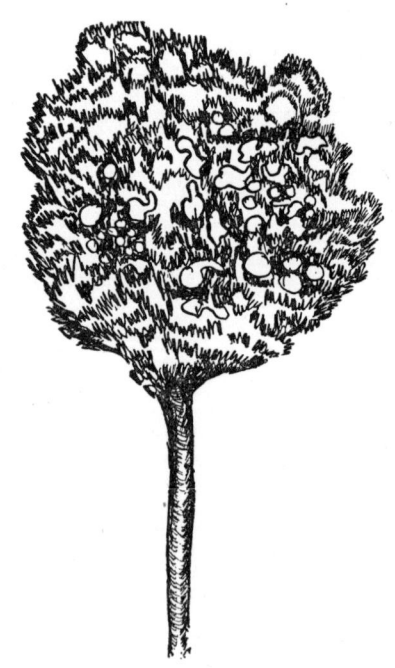

HOW THE SPONGE GROWS

THE VIOLET SNAIL

Dear Pussy Cousin:

I hunted all over the yard this morning for Freddie and Willie Snail; at last I found Freddie coming out from under a board. I started to tell him what my mistress told the children last night, about the violet snail that lives in the ocean.

"Wait a minute, Chum, until I find Willie Snail," said Freddie Snail. "He will be interested to hear about it, too."

He slid along on the slippery track that he makes, while I followed him. He soon found Willie Snail, so I told them both about the violet snail.

This snail floats on top of the ocean. It is a soft violet color that harmonizes with the blue of the water, which protects it from its enemies.

My mistress says that the shell of the violet snail will float when it is attached to its bubble raft. The mother snail throws out a substance which hardens as soon as it touches the water, while a bubble of air forms under it which keeps the mother snail afloat. Several of these bubbles form a raft.

The mother snail hides her eggs under this raft until they hatch out as baby snails, floating on the ocean with her raft of little ones.

When the baby snails become large enough to take up their life work in the ocean, they detach themselves from the mother raft, build a raft of their own, and float on the surface of the water.

The little bubbles help to keep these snails afloat and to look like the foam on the ocean. Even the sea birds who would destroy them cannot detect them with their sharp eyes.

Although the violet snail is such a little creature, being only one and a half inches long, it will reach out one of its suckers, catch a baby jellyfish, and devour it.

Sometimes when there is a land breeze, these snails are blown in to shore. Their shells are so fragile that they are easily broken. It is very seldom that one is found on the beach in a perfect condition. When a collector finds a perfect shell, he has a treasure.

I also told Willie and Freddie Snail that these ocean snails have a purple fluid which they throw out over the water to protect them from their enemies.

Freddie's long eyes stood out from his head so funny that I had to cover my face with my big paws to laugh.

"Why, Freddie, that is no more wonderful than the track that you snails make to walk on," I said.

THE VIOLET SNAIL FLOATING IN THE OCEAN WITH ITS BUBBLE RAFT

Willie Snail said, "You say, Chum, that they carry a house on their back, too?"

Yes, but they turn their house over, so that it will float on the water like a little boat and they ride in it and make a raft of bubbles to keep it up.

"Would the violet snail go to the bottom of the ocean, if it did not have this bubble raft?" asked Freddie Snail.

Yes, the bubble keeps the shell afloat.

"Why is it named the violet snail?" asked Willie Snail.

It is named from the color of its shell and its violet ink.

My mistress says that when she was on a ship off the Florida coast, she and the captain were looking out over the water with spyglasses.

"Look at that school of violet snails," said the captain to my mistress.

My mistress said that the water, for a long distance, was a deep purple, while the little bubble rafts looked just like sea foam. The violet snails were floating along with their little bubble rafts, quite unconscious of all the people on the ship looking at them. These people were very much interested in these little sailors of the sea, in their frail shells.

My mistress said that as the ship passed them, the captain lowered a bucket and drew up some water that was a dark purple from these snails' ink bags.

The captain of the ship gave my mistress one of these little violet shells after he had removed the snail. She keeps it in cotton and prizes it very much.

"Thank you for telling us about this snail," said Freddie Snail. "It was very interesting. I shall go among the snails and tell them how wonderful the sea snails are. We land snails have no chance to find out about our relatives that live in the sea."

Good night,
Chum.

THE WORM-EATING WARBLER

Dear Pussy Cousin:

Millie and I were so excited this morning as we watched a bird flying close to the ground, as though her wing were broken. She would turn over and get up and then fly a little way and then drop to the ground again, with her wings hanging limply.

My mistress was with us and all that she did was to laugh. Millie looked at her so reproachfully and I am afraid that I did too. My mistress is so kind-hearted that we could not understand why she was laughing at the poor little hurt bird.

"Millie, do not be so distressed, because that bird is only pretending," said my mistress. "She is one of the wisest little birds that we have in the entire bird family. She is doing that because we are near her nest, and she wants to take our attention away from it, so that we will not find it."

"You mean that she is doing that to get us away from her nest?" asked Millie.

"Yes, watch her now," said my mistress. "She will fly a little farther and then drop to the ground. When we come near her she will fly again."

We all went nearer. She flew away but still kept close to the ground, and then dropped, rolled over, and stretched out her wings.

"You rascal, you are trying to deceive us," said my mistress. "But you have not deceived me at all. I know just where your nest is. But we will go away and leave you in peace."

"She is one of the smartest birds that we have," said my mistress, as we walked home. "She builds her nest on the ground, under a stump, or near an old log where it is sheltered. She weaves pieces of hair, and grass, and bits of dry leaves very cleverly into her nest, and then lays from three to five creamy white eggs, with little brown blotches on them."

THE WORM-EATING WARBLER'S NEST CUDDLED DOWN IN THE TRAILING ARBUTUS

"I could see as she rolled over, that she was looking at us out of the corner of her eye, but not a bit as though she were in pain."

Millie begged so hard to know where her nest was that my mistress said: "Millie, if I tell you, I want you to promise not to go near the nest, or tell anyone where it is, because it only distresses the little bird."

"I promise," said Millie.

"You remember where the trailing arbutus grows in the woods," said my mistress. "Around the corner of that bank there is an old stump. Mrs Worm-eating Warbler has built her nest under that stump. The soft, little brown nest cuddled down among the trailing arbutus is a picture worth looking at."

This little bird is smaller than the English sparrow. She is olive above; the head is brown, with two black stripes running through the crown to the nape. She also has black lines running from the eyes to the neck, while the under part is buff flecked with white.

She certainly did fool us. If my mistress had not known that she was just pretending to be hurt, she would have been as sympathetic as we were.

If you ever see a bird performing in this manner, you too will think that she is hurt.

Good night,
Chum.

"GOOD MORNING," SAID THE HICKORY HORN-DEVIL TO THE SPHINX WORM, WHO I THINK RESEMBLES A DACHSHUND

THE UGLY WORM

Dear Pussy Cousin:

One should be careful not to hurt the feelings of others or criticize their personal looks.

I did not realize this when Bill Grackle and I were standing under the old oak. A big green worm, with spikes tipped with red, came crawling along the branch. Without thinking that I might hurt its feelings, I exclaimed, "Look! Look! Bill. Is not that the ugliest worm you ever saw? How can anything so ugly turn into a beautiful moth?"

The worm looked down at me. Then, with a toss of its head, it began to spin a silken web until it was completely covered.

I was so sorry that I had hurt its feelings.

Bill Grackle tried to comfort me by telling me that it did not cover itself up because it was ashamed of its looks, but because it was time for it to go to sleep.

It spun a silken case called a cocoon about its body. It passes through the pupa stage in this snug, warm house.

The cocoon is shaped like a hammock hanging close below the branch. It is sometimes called the cradle cocoon because it looks like a cradle. This little house is made of two walls of silk, with a matting of loose silk between, which protects its occupant from the cold of winter.

The worm will spin the silk lengthwise on one end and crosswise on the other thus making a little doorway on the end, which is spun lengthwise. This doorway allows the moth to come out in the spring.

We both watched the worm spinning its cocoon. The silken thread comes from a gland opening on its lower lip. It first made a frame for its home by stretching a few strands of silk the full length of its body. It then made a loose network upon these supporting threads. Moving its head back and forth, it was soon covered with this silken web.

THE WORM LOOKED AT ME AND BEGAN
TO SPIN ITS COCOON

You and Aunt Polly should look for some of these cocoons. You will find them on the branches after the leaves have fallen. If you do not have an oak tree on your place, look on the apple or plum trees.

THE CECROPIA MOTH

It is wonderful when you stop to think that in this little house there is going on such a change. The ugly green worm is turning into a beautiful moth.

Its name is Cecropia. Its plush gown is a soft, light, dusky brown. It is one of our largest silkworm moths, measuring from five to six inches across with its wings expanded. There is no gown worn by any of the moths that is more soft and beautiful than this.

These ugly worms are hatched from the eggs which the mother moth lays. Bill said that this worm outgrew its overcoat four times before it became full size. You will often find these little coats that the worm has crawled out of hanging on the tree.

I still feel that I might have hurt the worm's feelings, and wish that I had thought before I spoke as I did.

Good night,
Chum.

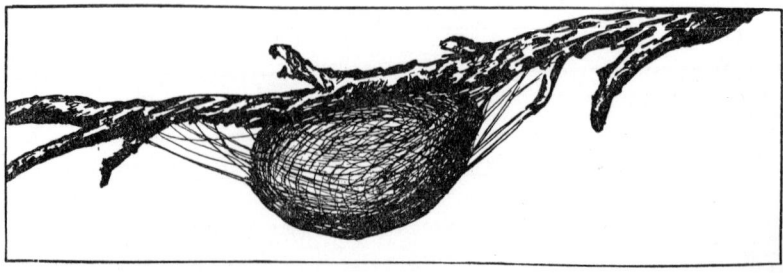

THE CRADLE COCOON OF THE CECROPIA MOTH

88

THE KINGFISHER

Dear Pussy Cousin:

The family went on a picnic this morning, up the river in boats.

I begged so hard to go that my mistress took me on her lap. The motion of the boat made me sleepy so that I went sound asleep.

I was awakened by a terrible screech, which came from a bird.

"Listen," said my mistress. "Do you know what bird that is? It is the kingfisher. It must have a nest on the bank. The kingfisher builds its nest in a bank or quarry. It digs a tunnel from two to four feet long, and makes a nest at the end of it. The nest is formed of the bones of fish that it has eaten during the year."

"A kingfisher dives for its fish," said my mistress. "It has a long bill which is very strong. Some of the fish that it catches are too big and strong for it to kill with its bill, so it beats them against a tree until they are a pulp, and easier to eat."

Mr. Kingfisher is very polite and always shares his fish with his mate.

"Look, there he is now on the branch that hangs out over the water," said my mistress. "He looks just like an old gentleman who boarded at the hotel. He wore his dinner coat in the morning, as well as a silk hat which was always brushed the wrong way."

I thought as I looked at Mr. Kingfisher gleaming in the sun that if Susie Meadow Lark could see the way his feathers were combed, she would never feel distressed about hers again. I suppose he has affected the pompadour, because he gets his head wet so much that it will not stay combed.

"Did you notice what stocky little legs he has?" asked my mistress. "That little white patch close to his eye gives him such a cunning expression. You are very good, Mr. Kingfisher, to hold so still and let us look at you."

Just then with a whirr, away he went and dived into the water. Up he came with a fish in his mouth. He flew over to the bank where we could see him devouring it.

Every little while he would give his cry—screech, screech—and his mate would answer from the other side of the river.

As we rowed along my mistress said that Mrs. Kingfisher probably had her nest over in the high bank. She is very practical and builds her home on high land so that she may bring up her family where it is dry and perfectly sanitary.

We have had a wonderful day. I am tired out so I will not tell you any more now.

Good night,
Chum.

MR. KINGFISHER

THE CURIOSITY OF MRS. TURTLE

Dear Pussy Cousin:

Mrs. Meadow Lark and I were talking in the tall grass, and the turtle did not see us as she came along.

Mrs. Meadow Lark said, "Wait, let us see what she is going to do."

The turtle walked up to the nest where the two little larks were asleep. She stretched her long neck and looked in, which awakened them, and they cried.

"Do not be afraid of me," said the turtle. "I would not hurt you dear little birdies for anything in the world. I have babies of my own. Oh, a number of them. When you get to be big birdies you must come and see them."

"Their mamma has been more thoughtful than yours. She has provided them with a little house to keep them dry, while you poor little babies have no cover over your home. I think it is an outrage to leave you down here in the grass without anything to protect you from the rain," said the turtle.

Mrs. Meadow Lark was so angry that she flew over to the nest. Perching on the edge of it she said, "Mrs. Turtle, I want you to understand that my babies are well provided for. They have everything that they want to eat, and a wonderful home, although it is on the ground. They are not burdened as you have burdened your children with a great house for them to tug around on their backs.

"All my babies have to do, when it rains, is to pour the oil from their oil pots over their bodies. This keeps them perfectly dry and is far better than to crawl into a dark old shell as your children have to do."

I felt so sorry for poor Mrs. Turtle. She was so curious to know what the little birds looked like, and was so happy when she peeked into the nest.

She hung her head and said that she would not hurt Mrs. Meadow Lark's feelings for anything, but that she did not know about the oil pot.

I tried to cheer her up, so I said, "Mrs. Turtle, may I see your babies? I have never seen little turtles and I would just love to go with you."

"Yes, Chum," said Mrs. Turtle, "if you would like to see babies that have to carry around a great house on their backs."

We walked off together and I said to her, "Do not feel bad. Mrs. Meadow Lark was all out of sorts this morning, because Mr. Meadow Lark fed the little meadow larks something that she thought would make them sick. I am

"DON'T CRY, I WILL NOT HURT YOU," SAID THE TURTLE

sure that she did not mean to be sarcastic. You know, Mrs. Turtle, one should never criticize others, and particularly their habits or the way in which they live."

"Children, children," called Mrs. Turtle.

Out of the mud in the pond came the jolliest crowd of little turtles. Each one was just about as big as a quarter of a dollar.

"Mamma, mamma, mamma, something dreadful has happened," said one little turtle. "A boy came along and took father away with him."

"Oh, mamma, what are we going to do?" said another.

I told Mrs. Turtle not to worry, that it probably was Jack

who had taken him. I would find him and turn him loose, and he would come home to them soon.

When I reached home I found the turtle. Jack had bored a hole through his shell and had tied a long string to him and put him in old Bob's kennel.

Curley, the squirrel, gnawed the string from the turtle, close to his shell, for me. The turtle thanked me and went home.

I did not wait to see Jack's surprise when he discovered that his turtle was gone. He told my mistress about the turtle. She said, "Oh, Jack, how could you? You have probably taken Mrs. Turtle's husband. He might have a family that he has to provide for. It is the same as if some giant had carried your papa away."

Jack hung his head. "I never thought of that," he said. "Why, all the fellows take turtles and tie strings to them. We never thought that we were doing any harm, or that it was making the turtle unhappy.

"I will tell every one of the fellows never to do it again. I wonder if that turtle will find his way back home. Do you suppose he will?"

"Oh, yes," said my mistress. "He is probably so anxious that he will go as fast as his poor little legs will carry him, directly home to his wife and babies."

I met Mrs. Turtle this morning and she thanked me. Mr. Turtle said, "After this, when I see a boy coming I will tell the children to hide in the mud."

Good night,
Chum.

THE LIFE HISTORY OF ORNITHOPTERA AMPHRISTUS

THE ANT COWS

Dear Pussy Cousin:

You remember I told you that I would write you about the aphids or ant cows. This morning I had a good look through my mistress's magnifying glass at an ant milking her cow. The ant cow held perfectly still while the ant rubbed its feelers back and forth over her back. Drops of honeydew came out of the little tubes on the ant cow's back. The ants are very fond of this honeydew.

The aphid or ant cow is a plant louse. It is found on the leaves of trees and plants where it sucks their juices. It is fond of the box elder and the maple, which have a sweet sap. This sap is changed by the aphid into honeydew, which is stowed away in a little sac that lets the honeydew out, drop by drop, when the ant rubs its feelers over the back and tubes of the aphid. So this is why the aphids are called ant cows.

If the sac becomes full and the ants do not milk their cows, this fluid drops on the leaves, making them sticky.

You will always see ants going up and down the tree or plant where the aphids are.

"We do not have to drive our cows to pasture," said one of the ants, "for they are good enough to stay in pastures green, and make honeydew for us."

An ant nurse came up just then and started to milk one of the cows. She then carried this honeydew back to the ant's home to feed the ant babies. It makes the little ants strong.

"We are not the only ones that are fond of this honeydew," said the ant. "After the aphids cover the leaf with this sticky substance you may see a chipmunk or a squirrel, with a leaf in its paws, licking off the honeydew."

"Yes," said the grey squirrel, who was up in the tree. "We call those leaves covered with honeydew our lollipops."

So when you see little black specks on the underside of a leaf, Cousin Ted, you will know that they are aphids or ant cows.

Good night,
Chum.

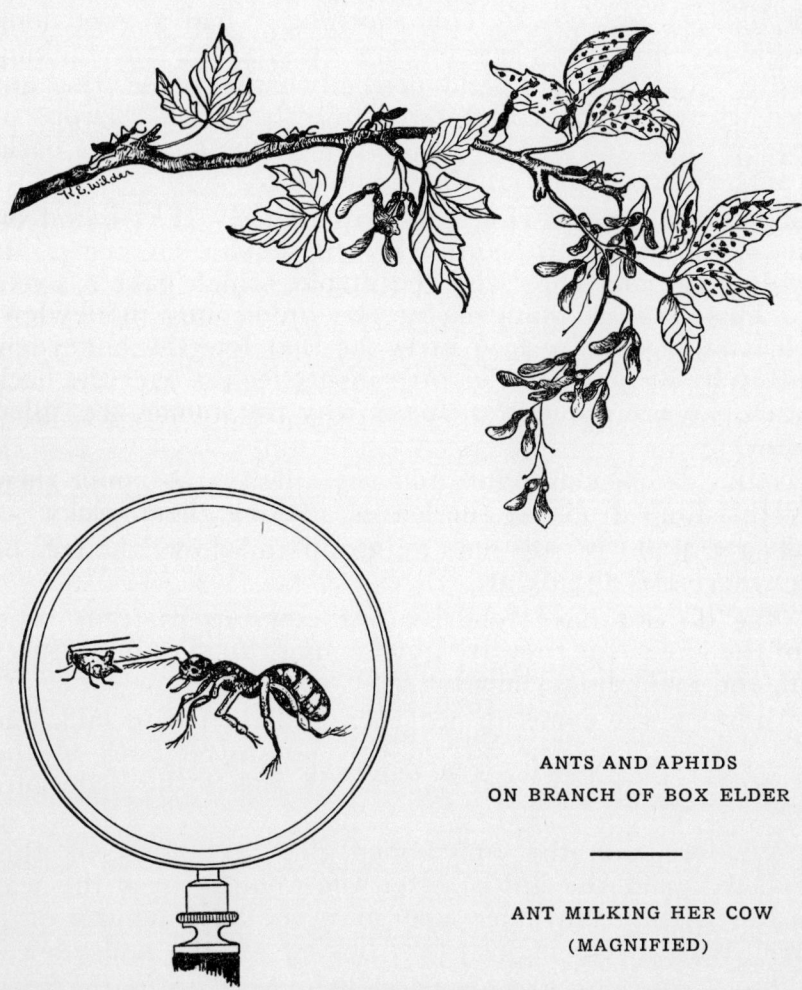

ANTS AND APHIDS
ON BRANCH OF BOX ELDER

———

ANT MILKING HER COW
(MAGNIFIED)

SPIDERS BALLOONING

Dear Pussy Cousin:

A little boy who is visiting here at the farm had a toy balloon. He was playing with it in the yard and let go of the string. Up went the balloon. I tried to catch it with my big paws, but it went too fast. The poor little fellow commenced to cry as though his heart would break.

Out came my mistress, who picked him up in her arms and said, "Don't cry because the balloon has gone. It is way up in the air where it will have such a jolly time, flying through the clouds, seeing the boys and girls playing on the ground, and laughing, too, because you could not catch it. If you will stop crying I will show you a spider ballooning."

I pricked up my ears, because the idea of a spider ballooning was new to me. I followed my mistress, who took the little boy to the edge of the woods where the lady's slippers grow. She stopped and said, "Look! See the balloons. Those are spiders."

He stopped crying and said, "Look, look, they are going through the air just as my balloon did."

"Yes," said my mistress, "they make their little balloons out of their web. Then they jump and their long silken threads buoy them up in the air. They like the sport of ballooning. All insects play just as children do. Even the busy ants and bees have their play time."

"Few people know that the spiders go ballooning," she said. "Yet they often see a spider web floating in the air, but do not know what it means. Those silken threads buoy the spider up in the air just as the gas bag holds up the balloon. When they land on a bush they lose their balloon too, but they don't cry about it. The spider just makes up its mind that it will have another, so it makes it and away it goes through the air."

The little boy said, "I like the spider's balloon better than I do mine. I am going to watch them. May I?"

Millie came over to where we were standing and was much interested.

My mistress told her that the spiders make a foot basket of their web; that in the spider's abdomen are the spinnerets covered with minute spinning spools, through which the liquid silk is forced from glands within the body; that these liquid threads harden when they strike the air, and are held apart or combined as the spider wishes.

"See, several threads are coming from its body now," said Millie.

"Yes," explained my mistress, "when the breeze catches them they will be drawn out several feet."

The spider bent its legs toward the breeze and stiffened its joints. Suddenly with a bound it mounted into the air and floated away with the breeze.

The threads spreading among its eight legs formed a basket, while the long silken streamers of its web floated out several feet above its body. They acted as a balloon which enabled it to keep afloat.

I shall ask Jimmy Spider why he never told me that the spiders go ballooning. Watch for them and you will see an interesting sight.

Good night,
Chum.

"LOOK!
SEE THE LITTLE BALLOONS,
THOSE ARE SPIDERS"

FIRE FLIES

Dear Pussy Cousin:

My mistress was sitting in the summer house with the children last night. I curled up in her lap, rested my head between my big paws, and watched the sky and the wonderful coloring in the afterglow of the sunset.

There were a great many clouds. The purple haze on the hills, and the mist rising from the valley made a beautiful picture.

It soon became very dark, for there was no moon. The fireflies or lightning bugs began to flash their little lanterns.

"Do you know what Jack and I used to do?" said Millie. "We would catch those darling little bugs and put the poor things under a glass to watch them flash their light."

"Tell it all, Millie," said Jack, "for I am ashamed of it now. We would go off to play and leave the bugs to suffocate under the glass. We never once thought that they were little living creatures who helped to light a dark, dreary night."

"One does a great many things thoughtlessly when a child," said my mistress, "and not because he wants to be cruel. If parents would teach their children to watch and study these wonderful things and get the real beauty from them, their children would get far more out of life."

"It is a peculiar thing," said my mistress, "that science has never been able to discover what causes the firefly to give light. It is a mystery that no one has been able to solve."

"There are thousands of fireflies flying about tonight. How beautiful they are," said Millie.

"The firefly lays her eggs on the ground. I have often turned up a stone at night," said my mistress, "or dug about a dead tree and seen the glow worms with their phosphorescent light. This little glow worm is the larva stage of the firefly, and the firefly is the adult stage of the winged insect."

"I wish that I could solve the problem of how this insect gives light," said Jack.

"Who knows, perhaps you will," said my mistress. "I know you are going to be one of the great scientists of your age, making all sorts of wonderful discoveries, for you are such a close observer of everything that goes on about you, Jack."

"I have always called them lightning bugs," said Millie, "and I believe that they take the electricity from the earth into their bodies, which are like little dynamos that make light, and generate it."

"My, sis, you have grown scientific," said Jack. "She may be the scientist of the family after all."

I asked the lightning bug how it made its light.

"We don't know, we just make it," it told me.

"In the tropics," said my mistress, "there is a species of firefly that gives a red light. It is called the railroad beetle."

"I would call it the danger fly," said Jack.

"Hear Chum purr," said Millie. "He approves of that name."

My mistress carried me back to the house on her shoulder. When I got into my basket I thought what a wonderful evening we had.

Good night,
Chum.

THE AUTUMN RACE

Dear Pussy Cousin:

Have you ever though what a jolly time the leaves have in the fall? They have stayed close to their parent tree, whose arms have rocked them asleep to the music of the wind. They have swayed and smiled at you all summer. They are now looking forward to the fall, when they will be caught with their brothers and sisters, by a gust of wind. It will laugh with them as they blow along in their gay race to the great unknown.

The three leaves that I watched this morning were turning somersaults over one another down the side of a bank. Each one was trying to reach the water first.

The oak leaf blew into the water and smiled back at the maple leaf, whose golden yellow gown gleamed in the sun. This leaf whispered to the east wind to blow hard so that it could win the race down the swift little stream, as it too dropped into the water.

"Ah," said the east wind, as it whispered to the pin oak leaf that was left on the bank. "Do not rustle so restlessly. I will pick you up, carry you far down the stream and you will win the race; for you have never asked me to help you win, or be favored in any way; but you have been big and broad enough to take your chance in life and try to reach your goal without the help of others and so you will reach it."

The east wind picked up the little pin oak leaf and carried it away out of sight, Cousin Ted. I ran as swiftly as I could down the brook side to follow it.

The east wind died down and there on the surface of the water floated the pin oak leaf and what do you suppose lay curled upon it. A wooly bear caterpillar who had gone to sleep on the leaf, never thinking that its cozy bed was going to be picked up by the east wind and carried so far away. The wooly bear caterpillar held on very tight as the leaf floated down the stream. I followed it to where the brook made a sharp turn. The east wind caught the leaf up out of the water and blew it with the wooly bear safely to dry land.

"My," said the wooly bear, as he crawled off the leaf, "that was a great ride. I never expected to travel so fast in my life and I surely thought that I would never set foot on dry land again."

I suggested to the wooly bear that he crawl to the fence post and curl up in the crevice, on the south side and go to sleep.

When the leaf was dry its restless, rustling made me realize that it wanted to get into the race again. Soon the east wind caught it up and away it went.

Cousin Ted, it won the race just as we will, if we do not try to take all from others and then give nothing in return.

Good night,
Chum.

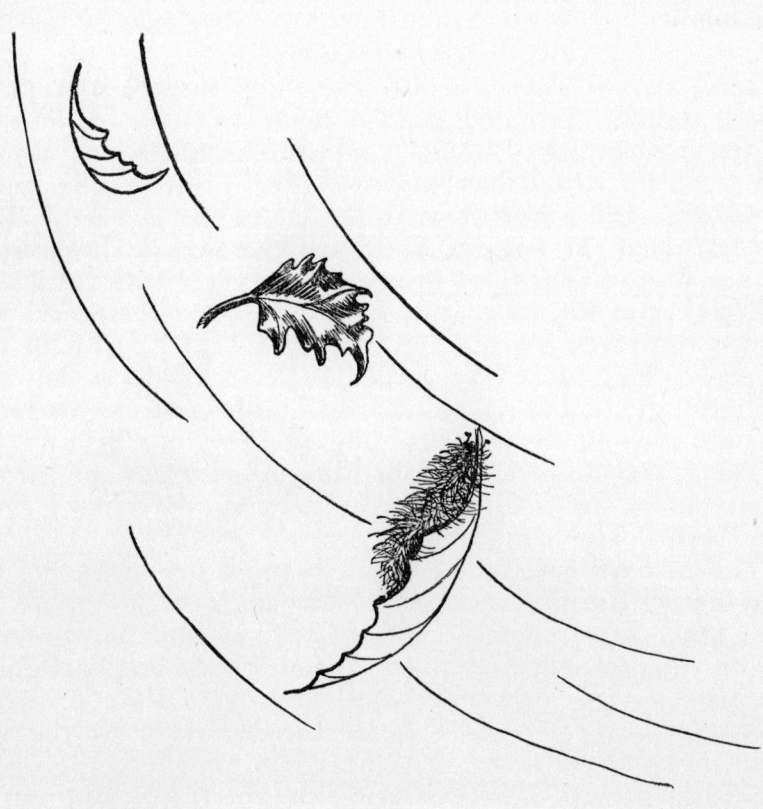

THE ROSE MALLOW

Dear Pussy Cousin:

I went to the marsh where the rose mallow and the marsh mallow grow. The rose mallows were beautiful with their big pink blossoms. The whole marsh was covered with them. The marsh mallow from which candy is made was also in blossom.

When I reached the edge of the swamp, I was horrified to see that someone had broken off the tops of a great many of these beautiful plants.

A violet-tipped semicolon butterfly was resting on one of the rose mallow flowers that had been broken off. The semicolon (;) is silver, while its wing is a soft velvety maroon, shading into a beautiful lavender.

"Good morning, Chum," said the butterfly, "I am so angry. An automobile stopped over there on the road a while ago. A man and a woman with three children got out. The man came into the swamp, broke off the tops of those rose

THE ROSE MALLOW AND THE SEMICOLON (;) BUTTERFLY

mallow plants, took a cord and tied them to the car. Now, Chum, you know perfectly well that by the time he got to his home, they would be all wilted. The only reason that he picked those beautiful flowers was to show when he got back to the city that he had been out in the country for a motor ride."

"The children were running around in the swamp picking the tops off of all of the rose mallow plants that they could reach. The woman turned around and said 'Throw those down. You can't bring them home. They are too short.' They then got into the car and drove away, leaving all this destruction behind them. They certainly did not want those flowers to beautify their home when they got back, or they would not have put the flowers out in the hot sun, but would have put them in the inside of the car and covered them up so that they would not wilt," said the butterfly.

"I sometimes think, Chum," said the butterfly, "that people do not come out to see the beautiful things that God has created but to see how much they can destroy."

I was sitting on the edge of the swamp, waiting for my mistress. She came along with Millie and Jack. "Oh, children," she exclaimed, "the rose mallows are out." And then she stopped and looked. She told the children what it meant to the mallows to be torn and rooted up in that way.

"We will not go any farther, but will hurry home and put these in water," she said, as she carefully picked up all of the tops that the children had broken off and wrapped them in wet paper.

That afternoon when I came into the living room my mistress had her face buried in the rose mallow blossoms that were in the bowl.

I rubbed up against her and she smiled down at me and said, "Chummy Boy, our rose mallows look as fresh and bright as they did before they were picked. They make the living room look very happy. I pity the people who do not appreciate the beautiful wild flowers of the woods, fields, and swamps."

I purred to let her know that I agreed with her.

Good night,
Chum.

EXAMINATION AT THE BIRD SCHOOL

Dear Pussy Cousin:

This is examination week at the bird school in the big pine.

Billy Grackle told me that I must not miss it, because Professor Owl is the head of the school and he examines all of the birds himself. Miss Wren is the teacher.

While we were waiting for the school to open, I was much amused to hear lazy Pete tell his sister, Betty Robin, and Susie Meadow Lark that they should not be afraid; that if they knew the subject to state the facts clearly because even if Professor Owl did speak to them severely, under that severity there was a kind heart. He wanted the birds of his school to realize the importance of knowing the subject and answering the questions clearly.

"The trouble with you girls," said Lazy Pete, "is that you are afraid of the old fellow, and hesitate when you know the answer perfectly well. You get nervous. Now you watch me. I will give the old fellow his answer straight from the shoulder."

When the examination commenced Professor Owl turned to lazy Pete and said in a very gruff voice. "Peter, from where does turpentine come?"

"From the pine tree," said lazy Pete.

"What else comes from the pine?" asked Professor Owl.

"Resin," answered Peter.

"Is there any evergreen tree that has an aromatic odor?" asked Professor Owl.

Before Peter could answer, little Jacky Crow spoke. "Yes, balsam fir." Then he was so frightened that he hung his head.

"That is right," said the owl, "but I addressed my question to Peter."

This made Miss Wren so nervous that she said, "Now birdies, when Professor Owl addresses a question directly to one pupil, no other pupil must answer."

104

THE TWO TEACHERS AT THE BIRD SCHOOL

Betty knew that it was going to be her turn next, so she braced her feet against the limb and looked straight up into the owl's face.

"Betty, how many needles has the long-leaved pine?" he asked.

TILLIE WOODPECKER HUNG HER HEAD

"Three," answered Betty.

"What are needles on an evergreen tree?" asked the owl.

"They are called needles, but are really the leaves of the evergreen tree; they grow in bundles," answered Betty. "The species of pine are identified by the number of needles in a bundle."

"How many needles in a bundle on the white pine, Susie Meadow Lark?" asked Professor Owl.

"Five." She answered.

"Is the white pine a hard or a soft wood, Tillie Woodpecker?" asked the owl.

"It is a soft wood," answered Tillie.

"What are pine cones for?" asked Professor Owl.

"They hold the seed," said Herbie Wren.

"Why is the pine called an evergreen?" Professor Owl, asked the little woodpecker.

She hung her head and did not answer.

The little Yellow Bird was so excited because she knew, that she stood up and flapped her wings. The owl said to her. "Keep your seat, Yellow Bird, until Miss Woodpecker has time to think."

Miss Woodpecker still hung her head, so he turned to the Yellow Bird and said, "Now you may answer, Yellow Bird."

"Because it holds its leaves all winter and keeps green from one season until the next. That is why it is called evergreen," answered the Yellow Bird.

Sentimental little Fluffy held up one foot and said, "Professor, I would like to say something."

"Well, say it," said Professor Owl.

"It makes the landscape more beautiful to have the pine trees keep green all winter, and furnish us birds with a shelter from the cold north wind. And what would the children do without their Christmas trees?"

"Very good," said Professor Owl. "These birds have shown remarkable training and you should be very proud of your class, Miss Wren. I should like Miss Meadow Lark to lead the singing."

The exercises closed with singing.

Now they are all anxious to know whether the pupils have passed their examination.

                                        Good night,
                                             Chum.

RUBBER

Dear Pussy Cousin:

Millie asked my mistress how rubber was obtained.

She told Millie that the rubber tree was tapped for its milky juice.

HOW THE RUBBER TREE IS CUT TO OBTAIN RUBBER

"Do you realize that we could not get along without rubber?" said my mistress. "All of the mistakes that we make when we write or draw with a lead pencil could not be erased without a rubber; nor could we ride for miles in our automobiles, in such comfort, if it were not for the rubber tires."

"Rubber protects us from catching cold, by waterproofing our garments. Mackintosh was the first person to combine liquid rubber with cotton cloth for waterproofing coats, an accomplishment for which his name will be remembered from generation to generation," said my mistress.

"Rubber is obtained from the milky juice or latex of many plants," said my mistress. "Some common wayside plants yield this milky juice, such as the milkweed and poppy, although these plants have never produced rubber commercially. The rubber that we use is a treated substance."

"Commercial rubbers are known by names taken from the countries which produce them as: Para rubber, Ceara rubber, and Lagos silk rubber," said my mistress.

107

"Para rubber is found in tropical South America. Para is a town near the mouth of the Amazon, from which much of the rubber from Brazil is exported.

"Central American rubber is produced from large trees of the nettle order growing wild in Mexico and parts of South America.

"Assam rubber is found on the lower slopes of the great mountain ranges of northern India. This is a tree in its native country, but is familiar to us as the small plants grown indoors known as "Rubber Plants."

"Lagos silk rubber is obtained from a medium-sized tree found growing wild in tropical Africa.

"Ceara rubber comes from a small tree. It is a relative of the cassava plant, from which tapioca is made. It is interesting to find that both of these plants yield a milky juice, one to make tapioca for puddings and the other rubber.

"In obtaining rubber from the Para rubber trees, a number of cuts are made in the bark with an axe. A little pail is fastened under each cut. The latex begins to run. At the end of a few hours the flow has ceased and the contents of the pail are transferred to a larger vessel. The liquid latex is then converted into solid rubber.

"A fire is made, using nuts of various palms. These produce a dense smoke containing acetic acid and creosote, which rapidly coagulates any latex exposed to it.

"A paddle is dipped in the latex and held in the smoke. The rubber forms a thin layer on the paddle. The paddle is again dipped into the latex and smoked. Another layer is deposited and the process is repeated until a large mass of solid rubber has been collected on the paddle. It is then removed and is ready for sale and export."

I whispered to the rubber plant in the living room and asked it if it was not proud to belong to such a wonderful family.

"I grew in a greenhouse and was as much interested as you were," said the rubber plant. "I am very proud to think that I belong to such an important family."

Put your claw into one of the stems of Mrs. S's rubber plant and you will see the milky juice from which rubber is made.

Good night, Chum.

THE DESERTED VILLAGE

Dear Pussy Cousin:

My mistress said to the children: "On our walk today we are going to visit a deserted village."

"Deserted village!" said Jack in surprise. "Where will you find a deserted village about here?"

My mistress laughed and said, "You will see a deserted village right on your own farm if you will come with me."

Millie caught me by the hind legs and made me walk wheelbarrow all over the room, saying, "Chummy, we are going to learn something about something. I do not know what."

"Come, we will start now, and Chummy can go with us," said my mistress.

We walked to the big locust tree, where my mistress stopped. "There is your deserted village," she said.

Cousin Ted, I have never seen anything so curious. All over the ground for ten or twenty feet about the locust tree were little piles of dry mud about an inch high, with round holes in the tops like chimneys.

"What are they?" asked Millie.

"They are the deserted village of the cicada, the periodical cicada, which is called the seventeen-year locust, because they live in the larva state for thirteen years in the South and for seventeen years in the North," said my mistress.

THE DESERTED VILLAGE OF CICADA

"The larva is a grub-like form that lives under the ground sucking the juices from the roots of the trees," said my mistress. "When it is ready to come up out of the ground, it forces the soil up and forms a little house about it so that it will get accustomed to the outside air. It remains in this mud house for some time and then comes out and crawls up the trunk of a tree, where it fastens itself by its hooked feet. The outside shell becomes dry and brittle and splits down the back. The insect slowly crawls out as the beautiful green cicada with the big ball eyes, which we hear singing so happily on a hot August day after all those years of underground life."

I was surprised, Cousin Ted, to hear my mistress tell the children that the grasshopper's real name was the locust and that the locust's name was the cicada.

The dogday harvest fly is also a cicada, having a very broad head with projecting eyes. This is the one we commonly see and hear in July and August.

The "seventeen-year" locust is narrow headed and darker in color.

At the grasshopper's family reunion I met all of the grasshopper's relatives, which were, you remember, the katydid, the leaf-insect, the walking-stick, the cricket and the cicada. These are all relatives and belong to the grasshopper or locust family. When you see them together, you can see the family resemblance.

I will tell you more about the locust tomorrow night.

Good night, Chum.

THE CICADA

THE CICADA OR SEVENTEEN-YEAR LOCUST

Dear Pussy Cousin:

I told you last night that I would tell you more about the cicada.

While were we looking at the deserted village, I spied a slight movement in one of the little mud huts.

"Look at Chum," said Jack. "He sees something in that hut over there."

While we were all watching, out crawled a cicada in its light brown shell. It made little creeps go up and down my spine, Cousin Ted, to think that anything could live under the ground for seventeen years before it made up its mind to come out into the sunshine and survey the world.

The cicada went to the base of the tree. After resting for a moment it crawled up the trunk until it was about four feet from the ground. Putting its hooked feet firmly into the bark of the tree, it stayed in this position until its shell became hard and stiff.

THE SHELL SPLIT DOWN THE BACK AND THE LOCUST CRAWLED OUT

We watched its shell split down the back. Out came the beautiful cicada, with its wings folded up close to its body. My mistress said that this was a very critical period in the life of any insect, for if it injured its wings in any way, while coming out of the shell, it could not use them, and so would be helpless.

The instinct of the insect to protect these wings is so strong that it comes out of the shell very carefully.

The cicada slowly spread its wings and inflated them, and then waited until they were thoroughly dry and stiff. They looked very beautiful as it stretched them out. They were so delicate and lacy.

Its body was like a piece of olive-green plush with golden-brown spots upon it.

Millie and Jack tiptoed to the tree where they could get a good look at the cicada's eyes. The eyes stand out from each side of its head like two great balls.

My mistress said that the hard, old shell, that the cicada crawled out of, would remain on the tree, clinging by the claws, until washed off by the rain, or brushed off by something.

"I have often seen these shells hanging to the trunk of a tree," said Millie, "but I never realized what they were."

On the ground lay a dead cicada. I poked it quite gently with my big paw. My mistress stooped down and picked it up. "Do not look so distressed, Millie," said my mistress. "Chum did not kill it. It has been stung by a wasp. The female wasp will sting a cicada, and lay an egg in its body, so that when the egg hatches, the larva will have something to eat."

My mistress took her pocket magnifying glass and turned over the cicada. She pointed with her hat pin to the two round disks, which she said were the little drums that are only found on the male cicada, as he is the one that makes the shrill noise.

"I am sure that all the insects enjoy his music," said my mistress, "I often listen to his cheery song. He seems to me to say, 'It's a wonderful world, it's a wonderful world; oh, why did I stay under ground so long?'"

So now, Cousin Ted, you know all about the life history of the locust or cicada. I think you will appreciate it far more than you ever have before, for it is a very interesting insect.

Good night,
Chum.

THE SILKWORM

Dear Pussy Cousin:

The silkworm said to his wife this morning, "My dear, it will soon be Easter time and all of the women are getting new bonnets. I do wish that you would discard that hood you have worn so long. Hoods are not fashionable any more."

Mrs. Silkworm turned to me and said, "Have I an old hood on my head, Chum? I have often looked at my husband

SILKWORM EATING MULBERRY LEAVES.

and wondered why he wears that old cap pulled down over his ears."

I suggested that they both come down to the brook and look into the water which would act as a mirror and give them their reflections.

How they laughed when they saw themselves. "We are not very good-looking, are we?" said Mrs. Silkworm.

"We will go back on the mulberry tree and eat a great quantity of the leaves and then spin our cocoons. Then we will come out as beautiful moths," said Mrs. Silkworm.

I followed them back to the mulberry tree. They ate leaf after leaf. I was surprised to see the quantity of leaves that they devoured in that one morning.

Mrs. Silkworm began to spin her cocoon. She was soon completely covered with her silken web. Mr. Silkworm was still eating. I asked him what those little black specks were on the mulberry leaves.

"Why, Chum," he said, "those are the eggs that the silkworm moth has just laid. One female moth lays from two hundred and fifty to three hundred eggs. They will hatch out into little worms with ugly hoods on their heads and caps pulled down over their ears."

"In Japan, the Japanese cut quantities of mulberry leaves and bring them into the feeding room where they hatch the eggs and raise silkworms. They are very careful to feed and tend to the little worms so that they will spin good cocoons. The more mulberry leaves that the silkworms eat the larger the cocoons will be. Then the Japanese take the cocoons and reel off the silk and make it into hanks, which they sell to the silk manufacturers. This is called raw silk," said the silkworm.

"It makes us very proud to think that this silken fiber that comes from our glands makes such beautiful fabrics," said the silkworm. "In the year five hundred B. C. silk was called the Queen of Fabrics."

"I am going to start spinning my cocoon at once," said Mr. Silkworm, "so good-by."

How I wish that you and Aunt Polly could have seen the worm's reflection in the water. There are folds of skin on their heads which really look like an old-fashioned hood on the female and like a cap on the male.

I can hardly wait until these silkworms come out as moths.

Good night. Chum.

SILKWORM SPINNING COCOON, AND MOTH COMING OUT OF COCOON.

THE BEE'S BREAD BASKET

Dear Pussy Cousin:

This morning my mistress told the children that the bees were gathering pollen.

"Let us go watch them," said Jack.

I whispered to one of the bees not to fly away, but to show the children how it tucked away the pollen in its bread baskets.

MAGNIFIED LEG OF BEE SHOWING BREAD BASKET OR POLLEN POCKET FILLED WITH POLLEN

When the bee lit on a flower, it clawed the pollen from the anthers so that it got it all over its body. The bee then gathered the pollen together with the brushes on its hind legs, and tucked it into its pockets, first into the pocket on one leg, and then into the other, using the opposite leg each time to do this. It then freed its body of the pollen, using these brushes, which consist of the rows of stiff hairs on the fourth joint and the underside of its hind legs, and the sharp teeth that cover the fifth joint.

After the bee had filled its pollen pockets, I followed it to its hive in the old dead tree.

When I reached the tree, the bee was scraping the pollen out of its bread baskets and mixing it with honey. It then filled the wax cells with this bee bread, but did not seal them up. It told me that the bee bread would keep better if some of the moisture evaporated.

The bee has a little prong on its middle leg to free its bread basket of pollen. It also uses this prong to pry the wax out of its wax pockets.

I tasted the bee bread, but did not like it. I see why people leave it for the bees and take only the honey.

When the bee finished filling the cells, the bee bread was dry enough for the bees to begin to seal them up. The bee bread will keep for a long time sealed up in this way. The bees are as proud of their store-room as a housekeeper would be.

When I came back, my mistress and the children were still watching the bees gathering the pollen.

How they laughed when they saw, through the magnifying glass, a bee with the two bread baskets on its hind legs filled with pollen. They stuck out and made the bee look so funny.

I told the bees about my suggesting a different color combination to the bee in my mistress's garden. How it stung me on my nose when I tried to lift it with my big paw!

The bees all laughed.

I can laugh about it now, too.

Good night,
Chum.

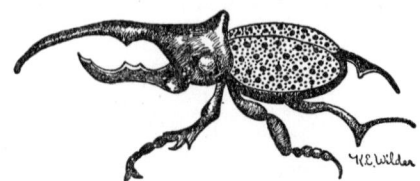

THE MALE HERCULES BEETLE

THE MARSH MALLOW

Dear Pussy Cousin:

I have had a wonderful day. We all went on a picnic. My mistress carried a box with her and she would not tell the children what was in it.

Along in the afternoon she had them build a fire, and cut some long forked sticks. She then opened the box and said, "Children, we will have some toasted marshmallows. We will toast them on the sticks."

After the marshmallows were toasted, they put them on crackers and ate them. Millie said they were delicious.

My mistress told her that it was because they were made of real marshmallow and not of gelatin.

"Real marshmallow, why, what do you mean?" asked Millie.

My mistress l a u g h e d.

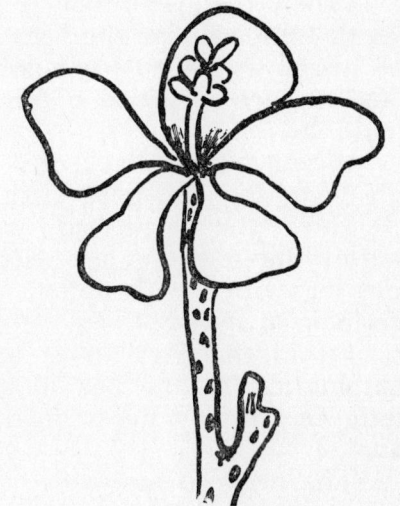

THE MARSH MALLOW

"Here are all my boys and girls on this picnic and every one of them has eaten marshmallow candy all of his life, and yet does not know that it comes from the thick root of the marsh mallow plant," said my mistress.

"Do tell us about it," said Millie.

So my mistress told the children that she had a secret that she was going to share with them all; that she had found the marsh mallow plants growing in the swamp the day that they found the rose mallow.

She then told them all about the marsh mallow plant. It grows from two to four feet high, with pink flowers measuring an inch to an inch and a half in diameter. The stems are covered with a velvety down that protects their breathing pores from becoming clogged by the dust and moisture arising from the swamp, in which they grow. All plants that live in a swamp must "perspire" freely to keep their pores open.

"We will make some real marshmallow candy from the starchy substance or mucilage found in the thick roots of the marsh mallow plant," said my mistress, "not the kind that you buy in the cheap shops, that is made from the white of eggs and gelatin, but real, true marshmallow like these you have all enjoyed."

"I remember the little pink-flowered plants that grow in the swamp," said Millie, "but I did not know that their roots were used to make marshmallow candy. We will save every one and let them go to seed."

Jack looked up at her and said, "I will dig up enough to make some candy."

"I do not think that the marsh mallow plants will mind a bit. They will be glad to be used when they are ripe. How much happiness they give boys and girls all over the country when they eat their marshmallow candy, or toast it in front of the fire," said my mistress.

Good night,
Chum.

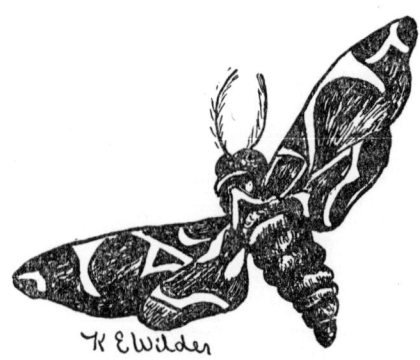

THE OLEANDER HAWK MOTH

THE SWORDFISH

Dear Pussy Cousin:

We are on board the yacht and the children are enjoying every minute. I have my special deck chair, which is a big willow one, with a soft downy cushion on it. It is under a striped awning. It is just like sitting on our porch. I can lie here and look out over the sea and listen to the interesting things that our host tells the children.

When Jack showed him the sword from the swordfish that the sea captain gave him, he told Jack the interesting life history of this fish, which I am going to write you.

"The swordfish is called the king of the sea," said our host, "for with its sword it conquers all of its enemies."

"The mother swordfish lays thousands of eggs on the sandy bottom of the sea," said our host. "Each egg is the size of a pea, and has a tiny black speck, which is hidden in the sand, so that these transparent eggs cannot be seen. But the crabs and the fish, with their sharp eyes, discover the eggs and carry many of them away, for they consider them a great delicacy."

"When these eggs first hatch, the yolk is attached to the little fish, which provides it with food for forty-eight hours," said our host. "The little fish have never been traced to where they live until they are a foot long, for they hide themselves so successfully that even their enemies do not discover them. All at once, when about a foot long, they will come forth."

"A peculiar feature of the swordfish is that they do not associate with one another. Each lives independently, although a number may be seen within a short distance of each other," said our host. "They grow rapidly, and when a yard long assert themselves in the fish world."

"I have harpooned a swordfish eighteen feet long, with a sword two feet long," said our host, "so this must have been a sword from an eighteen footer, Jack. One of these big fellows will tip the scales at four hundred pounds."

"I did not tell you, Jack, that the swordfish belongs to the mackerel family," said our host. "In fact, it is a giant mackerel."

"The swordfish's upper jaw is elongated into a rounded weapon tapering to a point like a lance, so that it is sometimes called the lance fish," said our host, "but the swordfish is the popular name."

"On the coast of New England, the swordfish is recognized as a food fish. It is regularly caught and sent to the market where swordfish steaks always command a high price and are considered to be a great delicacy," said our host.

"How do they catch such big fish?" asked Jack.

"A little platform is built on the extreme end of the bow of the boat," said our host. "The striker or harpoonist stands on this platform where he will have a clear view of the surrounding water. His aim is so accurate with this harpoon that he seldom misses his fish."

"It is a strange thing that this fish is not hunted or caught in any other water but that off the coast of New England," said my mistress.

"The swordfish is allowed to be king of the water in every other section, for there are none that dare dispute his title. He strikes terror to every fish in the sea, even attacking the whale," said our host. "Mr. Whale is made to realize that discretion is the better part of valor before this king of the deep, who wields his sword."

"I have always thought that the mackerel had a great many characteristics of the swordfish, for although they travel in schools at certain times of the year, they too hold themselves aloof from one another," said our host.

"I have ordered swordfish steaks for luncheon, but Chum will not have to eat them for he is going to have haddock," said our host.

I jumped up in his lap and patted his hand with my big paw, to let him know how I appreciated his remembering that haddock was my favorite fish.

I like the way that he rubs my cheek bones and then gives my ear a little twig.

I purred so loud that everybody laughed.

Good night,
Chum.

THE GREAT BLUE HERON

Dear Pussy Cousin:

The day that we were up the river on our picnic and met the kingfisher we also watched a great blue heron. It stood perfectly motionless like a statue, with one foot drawn up under it. For a moment I did not think that it was alive. Its coloring was a beautiful soft grey blue.

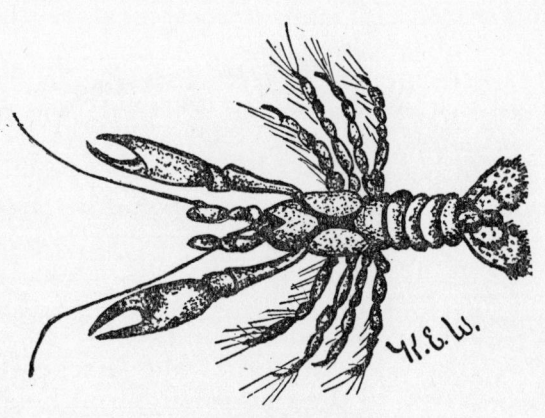

THE CRAWFISH

The children were so excited, for they had never seen a heron before. It is a large bird and stands four feet high.

My mistress says that it is an important bird for dike protection. The government has discovered that where it wishes to build an earthen dam or dike to keep a river from overflowing its banks, it must have a number of herons to protect it. These herons eat the crawfish which tunnel into the dike and weaken it, so that the river will break through and flood the surrounding country.

The herons will stand like sentinels by the dike and catch the crawfish before they do any damage.

They are just as expert fishermen as the kingfisher, but they fish in a quiet and dignified manner.

No wonder that the herons are such proud looking birds, for they feel the responsibility of protecting the dikes.

            Good night,
              Chum.

THE GREAT BLUE HERON WAITING TO CATCH A FISH

THE CREAM THIEF

Dear Pussy Cousin:

The cream thief has been caught. I must tell you and Aunt Polly about it.

The neighbors around here have been greatly disturbed by finding their milk bottles opened and the cream removed. Milkmen declared that when they left the bottles in the morning the cream was on the milk and that they were not responsible after the bottles had left their hands.

A meeting was called by the neighbors, and two of them offered their services to catch the bold thief by a silent and vigilant watch in the wee hours of the morning. They secreted themselves in a spot which gave them a view of the scene where many of the robberies had been committed on the unoffending milk bottles. The milkman was vindicated when they saw him leave a bottle of milk with rich, yellow cream, perfectly sealed.

Silently and stealthily, looking in all directions, came Robbin, a beautiful collie dog belonging to one of the neighbors. Sitting down on the porch before the milk bottle, he held it firmly between his front paws, biting out the pasteboard cover. Deftly turning it cream side up, he placed it on the porch. He inserted his long tongue in the bottle until the cream was gone. Picking up the cover from the porch he carried it to the street, dropped it and covered it up by pushing the dirt over it with his nose.

Aghast at the almost human instincts that he showed in covering up his guilt, they watched him go from house to house until his appetite for cream was satisfied. His little mistress, on learning what her puppy had been doing said that she could account for his not leaving the milk bottle covers, as when he was young she had taught him never to leave anything on the porch.

The families have all had shelves built for the milk bottles, placed high enough so that Robbin could not reach them.

He told me that he never saw people so mean as to object to sharing their cream with him.

"Why, Chum," Robbin said, "My ancestors barked loudly at Bunker Hill. They should not object to my taking a little cream. They had all the milk left."

Good night,
Chum.

THERE STOOD THE CREAM THIEF

THE EARTHWORM

Dear Pussy Cousin:

One day last summer, as I passed the back porch, I saw a tin can in the hot sun. I looked into it and found that Jack had forgotten to put his fish worms back into the cool ground. The poor things were nearly dead in the dry baked earth. I pushed the can off the porch with my big paw, and out came the earthworms. With many thanks, they dug their way down into the cool earth.

Jack has changed. He is more thoughtful.

A friend of his came over this morning and said, "Jack, let us go fishing. Come on. Dig some worms."

"No," said Jack, "I will get some liver from the house that the butcher has just brought for Chum. It will do just as well."

"The earthworms do so much good in the ground," said Jack. "They loosen the soil and make the ground open for the roots of the plants. Chum's mistress told us all about the worms last year. So I will tell you."

"See this earthworm. Its body is made of rings or joints. These rings are largest near the center, growing smaller toward the head and tail. Each ring has a tiny hook, which is used as a foot. The worm moves along by means of these hooks. When the worm wants to move it stretches its body to its full length and then takes hold of the earth with its hooks and draws up its body, and so moves along," said Jack.

"When digging a tunnel, the earthworm fills its body with earth and brings it to the surface where the worm discharges it. These are the little piles of earth you often see on the lawn just the shape of the earthworm. The soil takes this form as the worm presses it out of its long, soft body. Early in the morning, you will find these worm casts all over the ground," said Jack.

"A worm's home under the ground is made of long winding tunnels. These keep the earth loose for the fine roots of plants, and help to aerate the soil," said Jack.

"The earthworm eats dead roots and stems of plants which have decayed and become soft. It does not like fresh leaves, stems, or roots. When the worm gets the food into its mouth the rings begin to move in and out, pressing the food down into its body. A worm has two sacks for small bits of stone to grind its food," said Jack. "Worms must have water. When it is very dry they dig deeper and deeper into the earth to find moisture."

I PUSHED THE CAN OFF THE BACK PORCH WITH MY BIG PAW

"The worm has no ears or eyes, but feels the vibration of the earth as you step," said Jack.

"The baby worms are just like their parents, only smaller. These worms are born in a little bag of hard skin, which protects them," said Jack.

"Earthworms come to the surface of the ground in great numbers after a heavy rain, when their underground passages are flooded, to escape drowning," said Jack.

"Chum's mistress said that the earthworms are nature's cultivators. They loosen the ground with their hooks just as we cultivate the ground to hold moisture, for this makes plants grow. We should not destroy them, as they do much good to the ground," said Jack.

"We will have better luck if we use meat instead of worms," said Jack. "I look back now and think how I would leave the poor worms in a tin can to dry up and die. Since Chum's mistress told me about the real life work of the earthworms, I have the utmost respect for them."

"If a worm is cut apart," said Frank, "each section will grow a new worm."

"That is not so," said Jack. "The head part will sometimes grow a new tail, as the brain or nerve center is in this part."

"A worm's blood is red. The worm looks dark colored because it is full of earth. If it is kept out of the earth or in water its body becomes pale and clear so that you can see its two red blood veins. It must have fresh air to keep it alive. There are tiny holes in its body for the air to reach its blood and keep it pure," said Jack.

I stopped on the front porch and told old Bob the whole story about the earthworms and how considerate Jack had become.

Old Bob is very deaf and it is hard to make him understand. He was so pleased with my telling him that he rubbed his wrinkled nose against me. I realized that my mistress was right when she said that we should take pains to talk to and entertain old people.

Good night,
Chum.

MAPLE SUGAR

Dear Pussy Cousin:

Today is old Bob's birthday. How do you think he celebrated it? By going down to the big maple tree where he played when he was a little puppy. He had such a twinkle in his eye that I followed him.

The farmers grow a great many rock maples here, which they tap early in the spring to get the sap to make maple sugar.

I know that you and Aunt Polly have never seen maple sugar made so I will write you about it.

In the winter the sap goes down into the roots of the tree, where it is protected from the cold. When the February thaw comes, the sap rises, and the buds start to swell. The farmer then bores a hole an inch deep in the south side of the tree, about four feet from the ground. A wooden spout is put into the hole and a bucket hung under it. The sap drips into the bucket.

The farmer then takes the sap to the sugar house, where there is a big flat pan built into a brick stove. The sap is boiled in this pan until it becomes thick. It is then cooled, poured into bottles, and labeled pure maple syrup.

If maple sugar is to be made, the sap is treated in the same way, but is boiled much longer and stirred until sugar crystals form. It is then poured into moulds.

My mistress is going to send Mrs. S. a cake of maple sugar, so you can see it. Do not fail to smell it, for the odor is wonderful.

I rode around a while on the sled with the farmer who was collecting the maple sap. Then I went back to the tree where I had left old Bob. I have never seen him look so happy. His eyes were so bright and his ears stood up. I said to him, "Bob, why are you so happy?"

"Chum, I think that I hear the drip of the sap now. Do I?" he asked.

"Why, yes, Bob. I guess you do," I answered.

"I will tell you a funny story," said Bob. "When I was a little puppy about six months old, I ran away from my mother and followed the sled from the barn to where they were collecting the maple sap. I saw them empty the pail and I wanted to see what was in it. So I got up on my hind legs and put my two front paws on the bucket. Down came the bucket, spilling the sap all over me. How the men did laugh when they saw me. I ran and kiyied to my mother. She looked at me and asked how it happened. I told her, and she said that was what little puppies got when their curiosity got the best of them; that I must never snoop into anything again, and that she would punish me by not cleaning me; that I must lick myself all off and by the time I got thoroughly cleaned, I would remember that I must not snoop into things.

"Say Chum, when I had licked myself all off, I had all the sweet that I wanted for the rest of my life. I have

"DO I HEAR THE SAP DRIPPING FROM THE MAPLE TREE?" ASKED OLD BOB

never touched candy or anything sweet since. It made me so sick that I never snooped into things after that," said old Bob.

"Bob, Bob," called Millie as she ran and knelt down beside him and laid her cheek against his wrinkled old face. "Bobby, you must come in now, for it is thawing. You will get wet and your rheumatism will be worse. Oh, Bobby. You are eighteen years old today, and I love you, love you, love you."

I followed them into the house and old Bob sat in front of the fireplace with a happy smile on his dear old face.

He said to me, "I guess the children do love me. I am so happy and have had a lovely birthday."

Good night,
Chum.

THE JELLYFISH SWIMMING
IN THE OCEAN

HOW BULBS GROW

Dear Pussy Cousin:

My mistress and I spent this morning in her garden. She was uncovering the bulbs that she planted last fall. She lifted the straw and leaves from them so that the sun would warm up the ground.

"Their little heads will soon poke up out of the ground to see how happy they can make everyone with their beautiful blossoms," said my mistress.

Last fall when planting the narcissus, daffodils, jonquils, tulips, crocus and hyacinths, she said, "Now go to sleep and wake up early in the spring." She then covered them up with straw, so they would not freeze.

One of the bulbs told me that my mistress had taken such good care of it and did not let it dry out, that it was going to grow a lot of bulblets for her so she would have more bulbs to plant next fall.

You know, Aunt Polly, that the parent bulb grows little bulblets all around it. These bulblets grow all summer and in the fall are taken from the parent bulb and planted by themselves. Each one will make an individual plant and bloom. That is one way that bulbs are increased. When my mistress started her garden a few years ago she had only a dozen bulbs; now she has hundreds of them.

"Oh, Chum!" exclaimed my mistress. "I believe that this little crocus is going to smile at us today." There it was cuddled down in the straw, with its yellow bud peeking out between two green leaves.

My mistress looked down at it and said, "Oh, you jolly little rascal, I am afraid you have come out too early. I must not forget to cover you up tonight with some straw so Jack Frost cannot get you, for we are very glad to see you."

The crocus told me about the wonderful things that happen to the bulbs under ground. "Chum," it said, "we form our blossoms right in the bulb, so we are all ready to come out in the spring."

TINY BLOSSOM ALREADY FORMED IN SECTION OF BULB

It is wonderful to see nature awake in the spring. Each plant peeks up out of the ground with its gay spring clothes. Everyone is so happy when he sees the spring bulbs.

"You go to seed like other plants, do you not?" I asked the crocus.

"Yes," said the crocus, "and when the seed is planted, it takes from two to three years to grow a bulb, depending upon the variety. When the little bulblets form on the parent bulb, they may be planted the same year and some of them will blossom the following year. These bulblets will produce the same kind of a flower as their parent. The seed from the bulb may produce an entirely different color of flower, for when the bees visit the flower they may leave some pollen from another bulb flower. The seed is a part of each bulb, and so produces a color combination of both flowers. The bulb blossoms quicker from bulblets than from seed."

I wish that you and Aunt Polly could have seen the little crocus smile up at us.

Good night,
Chum.

HOW BULBLETS FORM AROUND THE PARENT BULB

MAGNIFIED SECTION OF A LEAF BUD OF THE
HORSE CHESTNUT TREE

THE LEAF BUD

Dear Pussy Cousin:

It was very cold today. I went out under the horse-chestnut tree and looked up into its branches. I asked it if its little buds were cold.

It answered me and said, "No, indeed, Chum. Our raincoats protect us from the ice and cold."

"Your raincoats!" I exclaimed.

"Yes, we call our outer scales our raincoats," said the tree, "for they protect us from the rain and keep us warm."

"But are you not cold at all?" I asked.

"Oh no, underneath our raincoats we wear a warm little jacket that protects us and our leaves. These leaves cuddle down against the warm packing around our blossoms. Our blossoms are all formed in our buds ready to grow. The warm packing is soft and furry, like a woolen muffler. You see with our raincoat, our warm jacket, and our muffler we are so comfortable that we don't mind the cold at all. The only trouble is that we sometimes get too anxious and peep out too soon, and get nipped by Jack Frost."

"In the spring when there is a warm spell the sap begins to flow up into our buds, making them swell; then our raincoats become too tight and burst. But if we stay cuddled down in our warm coats until the weather is settled and do not unfold our leaves to show our new green gowns, we are very comfortable."

I asked the tree what it meant by its leaves folding up.

"Don't you know, Chum," said the tree, "that the leaves are all in my buds now folded up like fans? They lie close together so that they can get inside of the warm packing where they are protected from the cold. Have you not seen the little fans unfold in the spring? They are very happy to open and see what is going on around them.

"The blossom is at the tip of the branch and stops the twig's growth. The side buds continue to grow, forming a new branch. The blossoms are a creamy white with purple or yellow blotches at the throat," said the tree.

"Another interesting thing, Chum, is when our petals fall off," said the tree, "the tiny little horse-chestnuts are found, at the base of the blossoms, in their green jackets. This jacket is really a tiny spined burr having the horse-chestnut with its conspicuous scar inside. The green cases protect our nuts until they become ripe, when they burst open and let fall the horse-chestnuts with their mahogany colored shells."

You and Aunt Polly must watch the swelling of the buds. The sap comes up in the spring after it has rested all winter in the roots, where it is warm and safe from being frozen. The opening of the leaves, the development of the blossom, and the formation of the fruit go on very slowly. We can see the change as summer goes on.

Good night,
Chum.

THE DRAGON FLY

Dear Pussy Cousin:

We went on a picnic today and my mistress had luncheon near the edge of the pond. What a jolly meal it was.

Millie looked out over the pond and told my mistress that she thought there was no more beautiful water insect, when the sun shone upon it, than the dragon fly.

"Here comes one now," said Jack. "It is beautiful. It is green, yellow, purple, and bronze."

"See its eyes, children," said my mistress. "They are wonderful."

We watched these dragon flies flashing back and forth in their gay flight over the pond.

When luncheon was finished my mistress said, "Now we will study the life history of the dragon fly.

"That female dragon fly has just dropped her eggs in the water where they will hatch out into lively, hungry larvae. We saw her hovering over the pond with the tip of her abdomen dipping beneath the surface. When the egg hatches it is called a nymph," said my mistress. "It has strong jaws and immediately begins to prey upon other insects and larvae that it finds in the water."

Focussing her spy glass on the bottom of the pond my mistress showed the children these larvae dashing back and forth in the water catching minute water insects with their prong-like jaws. Just then one caught a water beetle near the surface where we could see it quite plainly. It had a hard scaly shell and was easily distinguished by its wide head, prominent eyes, and broad abdomen.

"This larva," said my mistress, "is quite as active as the mature dragon fly. You know most insects in the larva stage are dull and stupid, but not the dragon fly."

"What is Chum looking at?" asked Millie. "He has been watching those reeds growing in the pond out there."

"There is not much that Chummy Boy misses," said my mistress.

Crawling up out of the water on one of the reeds was a dragon fly larva. When it came up out of the water, it reached over to another reed and caught its hooked legs into this reed. It was then firmly fastened and hung suspended between the two reeds. It rested a few moments, then it swayed back and forth with a rocking motion of its body. Its shell seemed to quiver, and suddenly cracked down the back and split open from end to end. Slowly the full grown dragon fly crawled out of its skin, leaving the dry skin or shell hooked to the reeds.

LARVA OF THE DRAGON FLY

"Now watch it closely," said my mistress, "and we will see what happens."

It rested again for quite a few minutes. As it dried, the colors began to glow in their full brilliancy, and the big eyes that a few minutes ago were dull now shone like balls of fire.

We held our breath in amazement. Suddenly the dragon fly began to pump air into the fine little tube-like veins that ran through the wings. Slowly these tubes filled and the wings began to rise from the body, stretching out on each side. The dragon fly filled every little vein with air. The wings were now fully inflated and I expected to see it fly away, but it did not.

My mistress explained why. She said it would wait until it was thoroughly rested and the wings were dry and stiff.

Jack timed the dragon fly's rest, and found that it was

five minutes by his watch before it suddenly raised its wings and darted away, gleaming in the sunshine.

"They are not always called dragon flies, but are sometimes called devils' darning needles," said Millie.

"Yes, and ignorant people think that they will sew up their ears," said my mistress. "They are also called snake doctors, because some people think that they can bring dead snakes to life. But, of course, children, these are the beliefs of ignorant people and are not so."

"I agree with Millie," said my mistress, "that the dragon fly is one of the most beautiful water insects. It should be appreciated. It has no sting, is perfectly harmless, and does a great work during its life in destroying mosquitoes."

This was an experience that I shall never forget, Cousin Ted. It has been a happy and interesting day.

I must go to bed in my basket now, for my mistress is calling me.

Good night,
Chum.

"MY, MY, HOW WONDERFUL," SAID MRS. HOP TOAD

THE ACCOMMODATING RATS

Dear Pussy Cousin:

One of the hens, which the children call Mrs. Hennins, and I have become great friends. She had made her nest under the wood shed and did not think that the spring rains would wash into it, but they did. She asked me if I thought that I could roll the eggs out from under the shed with my big paw.

I told her that I could but that I would probably break the eggs and she would lose her babies. While we were talking about the eggs, a rat appeared.

"I will move them, with the help of my wife, to a safe dry place," said the rat. He then called Mrs. Rat, who came and lay on her back. He rolled an egg on to her body. She held it with her legs. Taking her tail over his shoulder, he dragged her and the egg out from under the wood shed.

When Mrs. Hop Toad saw them coming, she held up her hands and exclaimed, "My, my, how wonderful! I have never seen anything like that. What are you rats going to do with that egg?"

I told her how accommodating the rats were; that they were going to move every one of Mrs. Hennins' eggs to a dry, warm place.

"Thank you, Mr. and Mrs. Rat. What can I do for you?" said Mrs. Hennins, after all the eggs were safely moved.

"Nothing, thank you," said Mr. Rat. "We were glad to help you out of your trouble."

I told them that I would bring them a piece of cheese. I went to the house to get the cheese that my mistress had given me. You know I am very fond of cheese. I brought it down in my mouth to Mr. Rat and his wife. They thanked me and had a great feast. I told them I would not eat my cheese after that, but would bring it to them, as I appreciated what they had done for Mrs. Hennins.

Good night,
Chum.

TEA

Dear Pussy Cousin:

The accommodating rat told me all about the Boston tea party this morning when I brought him my piece of cheese.

The rat said that his ancestors lived on Griffin's wharf in Boston harbor.

The Boston tea party was really the beginning of the American Revolution. Great Britain taxed the colonists so much for their tea that they rebelled. The Boston people held an indignation meeting in the Old South Church. They went to the three ships that lay in the harbor loaded with tea, boarded them, opened the cases, and threw three hundred and forty-two chests of tea overboard.

"My ancestors were on the dock watching them," said the rat. "Do not smile. My first ancestors came to America on the Mayflower. I know, Chum, that ship was very crowded and that practically all of the Americans had some ancestor that came over in it. But mine really did. Later they selected Boston for their home."

I told the rat that I had often wondered how tea grew and asked him if he had any idea about it.

"Yes, indeed I have," he said. "I know all about it." This is what he told me.

Tea grows on a bushy plant like a shrub. If it is not pruned it will grow into a small tree. The white blossom is very beautiful. The leaves are long and narrow.

The stems of the tea plant are used in China and Japan. They are shipped to this country in little bundles. These stems make tea that is too mild for the American taste.

Oil glands in the leaves contain an essential oil to which the flavor of the tea is due.

The original home of the tea plant has not been determined, it being either China or the neighboring province of India.

Tea now comes from China, Ceylon, India, Java, Japan, Formosa, and Sumatra.

The same tea leaves grown in any of these localities can be cured so as to make either green or black tea.

Green tea leaves are steamed to a certain temperature to destroy the oxidizing ferments which are left in black tea.

In manufacturing black tea, the leaves are spread on racks. This process withers them and makes them soft so the leaf can be rolled. Rolling breaks the cells and so makes the juices dissolve when the tea is brewed.

In some countries the tea is flavored with the flower bud.

I did not realize when I brought the cheese to the rat this morning that he was going to give me so much information about tea. I have always been so curious to know how it grew.

I even tasted it, but did not like it. It is just as well, because it is not good for cats' nerves.

Good night,
Chum.

THE LEAF AND FLOWER OF THE TEA PLANT

DAHLIAS

Dear Pussy Cousin:

Jack took a spading fork this morning and dug up the garden, where my mistress and Millie are going to plant the dahlias. He then brought a basket of dahlia roots from the cellar. My mistress separated the clumps and pulled off the single toes.

"Last year, when mother told me to separate the clumps of dahlias, she said that one toe would make a clump in the fall," said Millie. "I planted one or two clumps and never told her anything about it. These dahlias did not do half as well as the clumps that I separated, planting just one toe. I tied a string on this one toe last spring when I planted it and now see what a clump it has made."

"Let us count the toes in that clump," said Jack.

They did and there were nine toes. "Gracious, that is wonderful," said Millie.

"A great many years ago, certain species of dahlias were used in place of the potato," said my mistress.

"I do not see why anyone would want to cook a dahlia bulb and eat it, when they could get much more satisfaction by growing it for its beautiful blossoms. I know that I would much rather look at the blossoms than eat the toes," said Millie.

This made them all laugh.

"Millie, what is this one tied with a pink tape for?" asked my mistress.

"I labeled that one because it is the beautiful pink cactus dahlia," said Millie.

"You should have labeled them all so that we would know just how to plant them and what colors would harmonize with one another," said my mistress.

"I never thought about flowers harmonizing with one another until you explained it to me," said Millie. "I just planted my seed hit and miss and I am afraid that I missed a great deal."

"One can get wonderful color effects by planting their garden so that there is a definite color scheme," said my mistress.

"Now we will probably have a magenta dahlia next to a red one," said Jack. "What a color combination that would make!"

"Do dahlias have seeds?" asked Millie.

"Yes, but dahlias are like the tulips and other bulbs," said my mistress. "They grow and blossom more quickly from the bulbs and then, too, you know what color of flower you are going to have."

"New varieties are obtained from seed," said my mistress.

DAHLIA FLOWER, SPROUTED TOE AND CLUMP OF DAHLIA BULBS

"The seed is planted and grows into a little bulb. In two or three years the plant is big enough to blossom."

"Are these single dahlias that we are planting called bulbs?" asked Millie.

"Yes, they are bulbs, but they are more commonly called toes," said my mistress.

It is going to be great fun to watch the dahlias come up out of the ground. Some of them are sprouted now, so that they will be up soon. They are so glad to get down into the ground.

The magenta dahlia told me that the folks need not worry as the bulbs that they had planted on each side of it were white.

The white dahlias will make a beautiful setting for the magenta one.   Good night, Chum.

THE DOWNY WOODPECKER

Dear Pussy Cousin:

I missed Mrs. Downy Woodpecker for several days. I was worried about her, so I went up into the orchard to see if I could find her. There she was sitting near a hole in the apple tree. As I came along she said, "Chum, I have a surprise for you. Down in that hole in the sawdust are three little downy woodpeckers."

"Mrs. Woodpecker, are you going to teach your children to do the wonderful things that you do with your bill?" I asked.

"Yes, Chum, I expect my children to take up their life work in this world and do it to the very best of their ability. I shall teach them to go down very deep under the bark and get out all of the insects that are injurious to the trees. That is why we have such strong bills. We have to dig very deep sometimes before we are able to free the tree of the insects that are destroying it. I am glad that people realize more and more how much good the birds do," said Mrs. Woodpecker.

"When the little woodpeckers are able to fly out of the nest, I will take them up on one of the limbs and give them a lesson in getting the insects from under the bark of the tree," said Mrs. Woodpecker.

I asked Mrs. Woodpecker how she happened to think of using that hole in the tree for her nest.

"Why Chum, it was not my idea. All downy woodpeckers make their nests in a hole in a tree," said Mrs. Woodpecker. "We select a weak spot in the tree, peck out a hole with our strong bill, tunnel into the tree, and build a nest at the bottom of it so that the little birds will not fall out and will be safe from all harm. The hole is made only large enough for one of us to go in at a time, so that the little birds are not bothered by anyone."

"I hope that I did not bother them when I peeked in," I said.

"No indeed, Chum, they were asleep," said Mrs. Woodpecker. "Come and visit us again. I hope that the little woodpeckers will love you as much as Mr. Woodpecker and I do."

As I bade her good-bye, the little birds awoke and peeped.

Good night,
Chum.

"CHUM, I HAVE A SURPRISE FOR YOU," SAID MRS. DOWNY WOODPECKER

THE DANDELION

Dear Pussy Cousin:

Why is it that people object to dandelions on the lawn?

They were so beautiful this morning. The whole lawn was dotted with their jolly yellow heads. They looked up at me with such a happy smile. I think that they make a lawn beautiful.

I asked Mrs. Dandelion in the adjoining field why she did not ask the wind to blow her seeds away from the lawn, so that when they grew up their heads would not be cut off by the lawn mower.

THE FIELD DANDELION GREW STRAIGHT AND TALL

"Their heads will not be cut off," she said. "Flowers have a great deal of sense, you know. They will grow to just the right height, so that the lawn mower will bob over them."

When the lawn mower went over one of the dandelion blossoms, I held my breath.

"The lawn mower will not hurt us. We dandelions adapt ourselves to the conditions under which we grow," said the dandelion.

You can take a plant and put stones around it. It will grow up until it reaches the light, no matter how low it usually grows.

Flowers will turn their faces toward the sun, no matter how many times you turn them away from it.

"I do not believe that there is another wild flower that gives the children so much happiness as the dandelion," I said.

"Thank you, Chum. We try to," said the dandelion.

"We are very happy when they take our seed parachutes and blow them around, so that they come up next year."

"Our parachutes go out all over the world. My grandfather told me that our seeds travel across the sea," said Mrs. Dandelion. "We tuck them away in the hay, and in this way we are scattered all over the face of the earth. Boys and girls, no matter what country they live in or are visiting, see their friend, the dandelion."

"It is such fun for boys and girls to make curls out of our stems. You have seen them do that, have you not, Chum?" said Mrs. Dandelion.

"We close our doors up tight at night to save our nectar for the early morning insects. We blossom so early in the spring that the insects depend upon our nectar and we are very careful to save it for them, because in the spring it is hard for the insects to get any food," said Mrs. Dandelion.

"You called your seed a parachute. Why?" I asked.

"Because it is shaped like a parachute and floats about in the air like one. Just look at them, Chum," said Mrs. Dandelion.

I think that if people would only set the fashion to leave the dandelions on their lawn, they would be far happier when they go out and walk upon it.

Good night,
Chum.

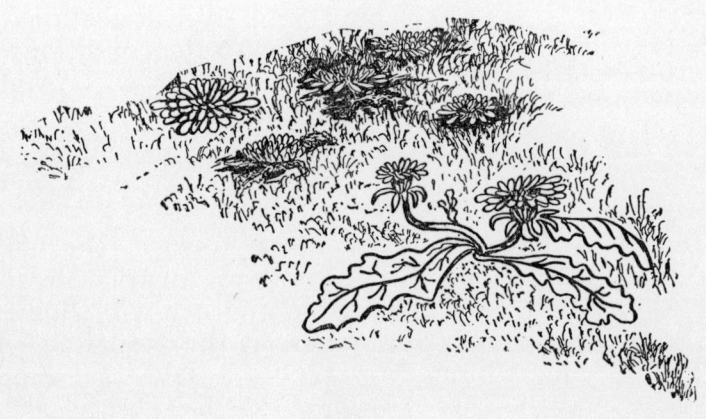

THE RED-HEADED WOODPECKER

Dear Pussy Cousin:

This morning Bill Grackle and I were sitting on the fence talking. Suddenly Bill said, "Look over there, Chum. That is the first time that I have seen Mrs. Downy Woodpecker's cousin, the red-headed woodpecker, over here on the farm. You stay here while I go over and talk to him."

So I sat very still.

The woodpecker was standing on a log, and seemed very glad to see Bill Grackle.

Billy asked him how it was that he had honored us with a visit. He said, "Well, Bill, I am not a bachelor any more. I have a lovely family which you must see. Two boy woodpeckers and three girl woodpeckers. My wife calls the three girls the three graces. We built our nest over here because we knew that it would not be disturbed."

"The children and the grown-ups on the farm love the birds," said Mr. Woodpecker. "They have fed and cared for us and we wanted to do something for them in return, so we decided at the bird's meeting this spring, that all of the birds should build their nest on the farm and help the farmer get rid of the insect pests that injure his crops. We are also doing a lot of reforesting for him by carrying the pine seed and dropping it in the wood-lot, which is now completely denuded of pine trees."

"I would like to have you meet Chum, Mr. Woodpecker, and know him as we do," said Bill Grackle.

So I came down from the fence and was introduced to the red-headed woodpecker and found him very interesting.

He told us that although his head was crimson, the little woodpecker's heads were grey. His lower back and wings were white, which makes a strong contrast with the black that extends forward to his neck.

"We talk to one another by getting up on a telegraph pole and tapping against the wood with our bill," said the woodpecker. "We have a regular code just as man has when he telegraphs. My mate will answer and relay my message to other woodpeckers farther away. This drumming sound that we make with our bill causes us to be invited to many bird parties, for it takes the place of a bass drum. We are going to get up a chorus among the birds on the farm and Billy Grackle is to be our leader. The junior class at the bird school is going to help us."

When Billy and I went back home, Bill said, "Chum, I think that your mistress and the children are giving the birds as much happiness as the birds are giving them."

Good night,
Chum.

THE RED-HEADED WOODPECKER LOOKED UP

THE RUBY-THROATED HUMMING BIRD

Dear Pussy Cousin:

A few weeks ago a ruby-throated humming bird came to the wistaria vine and built a nest. It was the daintiest little home that I have ever seen. It was composed of soft plant fibers and was covered on the outside with small pieces of lichen from the old rail fence, bound together with spider's web. It was three quarters of an inch in diameter and half an inch deep. Mrs. Ruby Throat laid two white eggs.

All of the animals and insects were so happy that the humming bird had come to live here. Everybody asked everybody else if he had seen Mrs. Ruby Throat and marvelled at her beauty.

The city children who moved in the old house where the chimney swallows had their home, came over every day and looked into the nest. This made Mrs. Ruby Throat so nervous that as soon as the eggs hatched she took the little birds away, no one knew where.

The worm that lived on the wistaria told me this morning that it heard her say that she could not stand the nervous strain of having those children peeking into the nest. While we were talking, the dragon fly came up and said, "Chum I have found them. She has moved her little birds into Mrs. Humming Bird's nest; the one that she used two years ago, up in the woodbine on the old tree. Mrs. Humming Bird is over there now visiting her. Mrs. Humming Bird is going to stay with the little birds while Mrs. Ruby Throat goes to the swamp, where the wild honeysuckle grows, to get nectar."

Mrs. Ruby Throat said that she had never been so happy. Every one of the insects and birds has been so kind to her. Even Mrs. Robin offered her nest. She hoped that her new home would not be discovered by the children.

Jimmy Spider spun her some web to bind her nest together, and Mr. Robin told her where there was some down to line it.

One of her birdies had such a fright from the little girl putting her finger in the nest and touching it. Mrs. Ruby Throat thinks that it will get well and strong again, if it is kept perfectly quiet.

Both Mr. and Mrs. Ruby Throat were worried about the little birds being so hungry and they did not dare to leave them.

Mrs. Humming Bird is going to stay near the nest and watch the baby birdies every day, while the Ruby Throats go for food and water.

Aunt Polly, I have never seen anything so cunning as the little humming birds were in that nest. They were so tiny.

I hope that the new children will play with Millie and Jack because they have learned not to frighten the little woods animals and birds. I am sure that these new children, when they know what it means to the birds, will be just as kind as Millie and Jack are now.

     Good night,
      Chum.

THE RUBY-THROATED HUMMING BIRD'S NEST WAS EMPTY

THE TADPOLES AND THE MOSQUITOES

Dear Pussy Cousin:

When I went down to the pond this morning, Grandfather Frog was sitting on a rock. He had called all of the little tadpoles up out of the water. "Now, taddies, listen to grandfather," he said. "I am going to make you the junior

"NOW TADDIES, WATCH GRANDPA CATCH A MOSQUITO"

members of the anti-mosquito society. The junior class made up of you tadpoles is now expected to take up its life work. You are no longer helpless little fish. You will soon lose your tails and be just like your papa and mamma. It is time for you big tadpoles to help the frogs of this pond clear it of mosquitoes."

"What are mosquitoes, grandpa?" asked the little tadpole that came up out of the water.

Grandfather Frog then told them how the mosquitoes form. They lay their eggs, which hatch out as larvae. These larvae live in the water until they are old enough to come to the surface in their little shell boats, and fly out as full grown mosquitoes.

"Now that you know all about mosquitoes, I am going to show you how to catch them with your tongue," said Grandfather Frog. "See, our tongue is hung in the front of the mouth, instead of in the back. It has a little hinge that lets it fly out of the mouth. The end of it is covered with a sticky substance which holds any insect. To catch it, we dart the tongue out at it. We are a great help to this world by keeping down the insects that make people's lives miserable."

"Now you little taddies will lose your tails in a day or two. Then you can hop out of the water and catch mosquitoes, just as grandpa showed you. Then Mr. Mosquito will not have a chance to bite the people of this town and make them uncomfortable."

"We frogs will soon rid this pond of all the mosquitoes. The hop toads and the tree toads are going to help on land," said Grandfather Frog.

You remember I wrote you about the anti-mosquito society that was formed by the hop toads, the tree toads, and the frogs to rid this town of mosquitoes. Now that the junior society has been formed, you and Aunt Polly may come to visit us next summer and you will not see a mosquito.

Good night,
Chum.

THE THIN MEMBRANE
BENEATH THE THROAT OF THE TREE TOAD
SWELLS WHEN IT SINGS

SECTION OF UNDERGROUND NEST OF THE MINER WASP

THE MINER WASPS

Dear Pussy Cousin:

While on a picnic this morning, we watched the miner wasps build their nest. Millie and Jack were very much interested to see the wasp loosen the ground with its two front feet. It then threw the earth back with its hind legs until it had made a small hole.

My mistress said that the miner wasps make a tunnel down in to the ground for about two inches and then turn it, to make a room at the end. They sometimes make two or three branches in one tunnel, and then lay an egg in each room.

After Mrs. Wasp gets enough dirt out of the hole she carefully covers it up with a leaf, a stick, and a few blades of grass. My mistress said that she does this so no one can find it. Before sealing it up, she finds something to put into the nest for food for the baby wasp when it hatches out.

The wasp that we were watching brought a caterpillar, which she put into the nest. She then laid an egg, and closed up the nest with little pellets of dirt, putting one on top of the other to form a little chimney.

"They are called miner wasps because they work underground," said my mistress.

"Do they sting?" asked Millie.

"Yes, they will sting if you bother them," said my mistress, "but no wasp or bee will sting unless you do something to disturb it or make it angry. The sting is its only means of defense."

The baby wasp, after it hatches out of the egg, eats its stored food, moults, and changes into a pupa, which finally comes out as a wasp. It has to make its own way out through the tunnel and gnaw open the doorway.

These wasps are interesting. Do you not think so?

Good night,
Chum.

HEMP

Dear Pussy Cousin:

Millie was skipping rope and my mistress asked her if she knew where the rope came from.

"Yes, from Clark's General Store," she answered.

My mistress laughed and said, "No, Millie. That is not what I mean. Rope is made from hemp that grows."

"Does it really?" asked Millie. "I never thought about it."

"That is the trouble," said my mistress. "Boys and girls do not think about nature providing everything for them."

"How does hemp grow and what do they do to make it into rope?" asked Millie.

My mistress then told her.

Hemp is the fiber of a plant of western Asia. It belongs to the nettle family. Like flax it was cultivated for centuries before the Christian era. Next to flax it was the most important vegetable material until the introduction of cotton and jute.

I TURNED MY BACK UPON THE ROPE

The hemp growing countries are Russia, Austria, Italy, Turkey, China, Japan, and the United States.

The hemp plant grows from four to ten feet high. The finest grades of hemp come from Italy. Great care is taken in preparing the seed bed and in growing the plant. The hemp is ready to harvest when the tops turn yellow. The male plants yield the best fiber and are cut before the female. The stems are made into bundles and put on racks to dry. They are then retted in water. After the retting is complete the stems are dried either in the open air, a process which results in a fiber of superior color, or by heat. The stem is then beaten by hand to remove the outer bark.

The best varieties of hemp are creamy white in color, lustrous, soft and pliable. This fiber is used as a substitute for flax, except for the finest linens. It is used for the medium grades of all goods made from flax. It is also used for cord, rope, fishing lines, and in the carpet and rug trades.

Manila rope is made from Manila hemp, which comes from the leaf sheaths of a non-edible banana found in the Philippines. The plants grow from eight to twenty feet high. The "stem" is composed of overlapping leaf-sheaths. When the flower bud forms, the plant is cut close to the ground. The leaf-sheaths are stripped off, cut into horizontal layers about a quarter of an inch thick, and then split into strips about two inches wide. The fiber is then freed from the pulp of the leaf tissue, leaving it clean and white.

The finest grades of manila hemp are of a light buff color, lustrous, and strong. The fibers are from six to twelve feet long.

The fiber is so strong that it is used for cables and ropes that require great strength.

Jack then said, "Come on, Millie, let us make Chum jump rope."

So they stretched the jumping rope from the piazza rail to a tree. My mistress put me down in front of the rope and told me to jump it. Over it I went. How the children did clap their hands and laugh. I jumped it to please my mistress, because she is so proud of my tricks.

The children kept me jumping the rope until I became so tired that I turned my back on it. They tried to get me to show off some more, but I would not do it.

Jumping rope is fun. I do not wonder that the children like it.

I was glad to hear what rope is made of, because I have a hemp string with a piece of paper tied to it. It is hung from the center of the doorway. I bat it with my big paw, a sport which develops my muscle and keeps me in training. They call it my punching bag.

Good night,
Chum.

JACK-IN-THE-PULPIT

Dear Pussy Cousin:

How I wish you could have heard the wonderful music in the woods. The birds sang their Easter carols around Jack-in-the-pulpit, and the insects were there too. Everyone entered into the Easter spirit. They sang their carols so joyously.

I must tell you what Jack-in-the-pulpit told them about doing kind little acts for others every day. He said that they count more in our lives than doing some big thing that everyone will praise us for.

"Sitting here in my pulpit," said preacher Jack, "I see and hear a great many things that the bird and insect world think that I pass by, but indeed I do not.

"Grandpa and Grandma Robin started to build their nest this spring. They are both old and are not strong enough to carry the big sticks. Betty and Peter Robin came over and said, 'You and grandma sit on the limb. We will carry the sticks for you.' Betty and Peter worked all the morning, helping grandpa and grandma build their nest. They were so thoughtful not to make them feel that they were getting old. When they got the heavy sticks in place they said, 'Now grandpa and grandma, you weave the grass. We just wanted to help and be a part of the new home,' said Betty. It is the thoughtful things like this that make us happy," said preacher Jack.

"Little Susie Meadow Lark, instead of coming here this morning to sing Easter carols with us, went to make a sick old lady happy by singing in the tree close by her window. Think of the joy that she must have given the dear old soul by singing all of the carols. This was a real sacrifice, because you know how Susie has looked forward to singing the Easter carols with us," said preacher Jack.

"This afternoon the whole robin family have gone down to the children's hospital. They are going to make the children happy who could not go out to Sunday school today, by singing carols to them. These kind and thoughtful things make up our lives and give us happiness that we cannot get in any other way," said preacher Jack.

Millie and Jack worked for three days coloring Easter eggs for the children's hospital. They made candy eggs and dipped them in cholocate for all of the poor children that could not afford to buy Easter eggs.

One little girl in the hospital said that the music had lasted all day. Between the birds, the children from the Sunday school, who came and sang their carols, and the happy faces of the flowers, she had a wonderful Easter day. She appreciated everyone's being so kind and thoughtful, but when the birds came to sing to her, she liked them best of all. Her joyous day was all due to the thoughtful children and the little birds.

Good night,
Chum.

PREACHER JACK IN HIS PULPIT

THE HORSESHOE CRAB

Dear Pussy Cousin:

Jack asked my mistress if she had ever seen a horseshoe crab.

"Yes, Jack," she answered, "I have seen them on the beach many times."

"What do they look like?" asked Jack.

"Their shell is a soft brown. Sometimes I have seen these crabs a foot long. I remember when I was a child

THE HORSESHOE CRAB, SHOWING ITS BREATHING GILLS AND HORSESHOE

playing on the beach a big wave came in and washed a horseshoe crab up on the beach and turned it over on its back. I ran down to look at it. As it was on its back, I supposed that the poor crab could not turn over. Suddenly it stuck its long pointed tail down in the sand and turned over. It did this so quickly that it frightened me and I ran back to the sand dunes where I could watch it as it crawled along," said my mistress.

"The king or horseshoe crab belongs to the Crustacea, and is a member of the scorpion and spider family.

"The horseshoe crab is ancient, for its fossil remains are found in rock deposits.

"When the crab is on its back, its four pairs of legs, and its five pairs of appendages bearing the book gills or breathing organs may be seen. These are called book gills, because they are composed of many thin plates, like the leaves of a book.

"The horseshoe crab delights in deep water. It is a burrowing animal, living in the sand. When it burrows the forward edge of its shield is pressed downward and shoved forward. The point of the tail is the fulcrum, as it pierces the sand while the feet are active, scratching up and pushing out the earth.

"The crab feeds on mollusks and marine worms, which are captured as the crab burrows in the mud or sand.

"The most interesting thing about the horseshoe crab is that the under side is shaped like a horseshoe. That is why it is called the horseshoe crab instead of the king crab, which is its other name.

"The little baby horseshoe crabs are very cunning. I hope that when we are at the beach next summer we will find one so that Jack can put it into his collection," said my mistress.

I wonder if they are as lucky as a horse shoe to find.

Good night,
Chum.

THE EASTER PARADE

MR. AND MRS. YELLOW-BILLED CUCKOO

THE YELLOW-BILLED CUCKOO

Dear Pussy Cousin:

The farmer said to my mistress this morning at the breakfast table, "I see that the yellow-billed cuckoos have come back this year. I am glad to see them. Four years ago the tent caterpillar infested my orchard and completely denuded the trees. The yellow-billed cuckoos soon appeared, and in a short time rid the orchard of the tent caterpillar. The yellow-billed cuckoo does not eat all of the tent caterpillars that it kills, but mashes them with its bill until they are all destroyed."

The only cuckoo bird that I have ever seen is the cuckoo bird in our clock. I have a lot of fun with it. I have not yet discovered how it knows the exact time to bob out of its little door in the clock and say "cuckoo." I have tried to put my big paw into the door to see what is behind it, but the cuckoo always closes it so quickly that I have never had a chance. So when I went out into the orchard this morning, I asked Mrs. Woodpecker if she had ever seen the cuckoo.

"They live over in that big oak," she said.

As I was going home, there on the oak sat Mrs. Yellow-billed Cuckoo. Mr. Cuckoo brought her a worm, and said, "Eat it, my dear. It will do you good."

They are both very pretty birds. The upper part of their body is drab. The tail feathers are black, spotted with white.

I was glad to hear that they do so much good in the orchard.

The clock cuckoo has a shorter tail. I suppose that is because it lives in the clock and does not have room for a longer one.

When the cuckoo in the clock came out at four o'clock, and said "cuckoo" at me, I tried to tell it what a wonderful bird its namesake was, but it closed the door right in my face. It was not very polite, was it?

Good night, Chum.

WHAT ONE SHOULD KNOW ABOUT A SEED

Dear Pussy Cousin:

Millie found some ripe seeds of the columbine. She was putting them into a bottle and screwing the cork in as tight as she could.

My mistress watched her for a few moments, and then said, "Millie, I thought you wanted to take those seeds home and plant them in the wild garden."

"I do," said Millie.

"Do you realize that those seeds are living, breathing, seed people and that the mother plant has provided them with a lunch so that they will not be hungry, and that they must have air to breathe just as you do, Millie?" said my mistress. "You are going to smother those little seed people to death."

Out came the cork of the bottle. Millie's blue eyes were very big and round and solemn-looking as she said, "Oh! I did not mean to smother them."

Pulling the curly head down on her shoulder, my mistress said, "How often we forget that the little seeds of the tree or plant are breathing, living things sent by God to fill the earth with plant life.

"These little seeds that are the offspring of the tree, plant, or bush have many struggles to get a start in life on account of thoughtless people who think that they are only seeds and do not know that they are little breathing plant souls that mean much to Mother Earth. We should protect and guard them and do what we can to give them a fair start in life."

"Seeds must breathe," said my mistress, "but of course they have no lungs as you have, Millie. When they are shut up away from the air they cannot breathe and so they die. Many foolish people who have shut these seeds up away from the air think that the seeds did not germinate because the bees did not pollinate the flower that these seeds came from. The bees have done their part, but the person whose

THE KINDERGARTEN SINGING CLASS
AT THE BIRD SCHOOL
"NOW ALL TOGETHER," SAID THE SINGING TEACHER

hands the unfortunate little seed has fallen into did not know that this seed was a living, breathing thing."

"The seed takes oxygen from the air. No matter how dry a seed may be, if it is alive, it is continually taking a little bit of oxygen out of the air," said my mistress.

Now I know, Cousin Ted, why they had to have so many cats in the seed houses: to prevent the rats and mice from eating the seeds. I wondered at the time why these people did not make tight metal boxes for their seed and shut them up so that the mice could not get them. It was because the seed must have air to breathe, whereas if they were shut up tight they would suffocate and die.

"I have always told you, Millie," said my mistress, "that in making your seed bed you must work the soil up fine and make it loose so that the air can get through it to the seed, for the seed requires much more oxygen when it starts to grow than it did while waiting to be planted."

When seeds are planted in the ground they swell, for they are taking up lots of moisture which stretches their skins until they burst open.

"What do you think is inside one of these little seeds?" asked my mistress. "A lunch put up by the parent plant, who realizes that while the little seed is sprouting, it cannot get anything to eat until its root grows long enough to take food and moisture from the soil. So the mother plant fills the seed's bread box with enough food to last it until the tiny plant is able to provide for itself," said my mistress.

The cotton plant mother gives an oil to the cottonseed to provide food for it while it starts on its life work. This oil is pressed out of the cottonseed and is sold commercially as cottonseed oil. We are really taking the food that the mother cotton plant has provided for the growth of the little seed when we use cottonseed oil. Rice is given starch to start its little seeds. The wheat seed is also provided with a lunch of starch.

"So you see, Millie, that it is necessary for people to know these important things about a seed so that they may help it to start on its journey of life with as little a handicap as possible," said my mistress.

Good night,
Chum.

WHEN WE PLANT SEEDS

Dear Pussy Cousin:

"We all have our ups and downs in life. The poor little seed that is thrown into the ground with no care as to whether its head is up or its feet are down, has to do a great many gymnastic tricks under the ground so that it may grow with its head up and its feet down," said my mistress.

If it were not for the instinct of the little seed that has landed head down in the ground, it would not grow up at all.

A seed has a top and a bottom. From the top the sprout or green shoot grows, that pushes its way up and up until it peeks out of the ground. It keeps on growing until it forms the stalk of the plant, after which it sends out side shoots whose tips grow, for it is the tip ends that are the growing part of the plant.

The root of the plant is growing down into the ground in search of water and dissolved minerals to be taken into the plant through the tiny tips of the root.

The green leaves manufacture food for the plant, with the help of the sunshine.

The instinct of this little seed is so strong, that if it is planted with its head down, its new root will turn and grow down instead of up, while the little green stem will twist and turn until it can grow up instead of down.

It is very fortunate for us who do not care whether we plant the little seed on its head or on its feet that this instinct given to the seed by a higher power is so strong that both ends of the seed will grow in the right direction.

You remember that the mother plant has provided food to carry this seed through the period of sprouting. This food is devoured by the hungry little seed, which gives it strength to sprout and grow.

Plants build up their tissues from the compounds of four chemical elements: oxygen, hydrogen, carbon, and nitrogen.

The plant obtains its oxygen and hydrogen from water; the carbon from a gas found in the air called carbon dioxide, which is the gas that people breathe out; while the nitrogen is obtained from the decayed parts or remains of vegetable and animal substances in the soil. Nitrogen is also found in the roots of certain plants, like peas and clover. You remember I wrote you about the clover plant, where the nodules of nitrogen were found upon the clover roots. Each little nodule is a house full of living bacteria that gives the necessary nitrogen.

How little we realize when we look at the tiny seed floating through the air, or the seed that we are planting, that in this seed are all of these wonderful things which mean so much to the earth and its people.

This little seed, when it starts on its journey of life, has to combat all of the stupidity of man, and no matter what its struggles are for existence it goes bravely on to carry out its life work, which is to beautify the world and to provide food for man so that he may have the strength to carry on his life work.

All that the little seed asks man to do is to let it grow for him. In return man should give a little thought to this brave seed whose journey through life means so much to him and to Mother Earth.

Good night,
Chum.

LITTLE MISS WREN, THE TEACHER AT THE BIRD SCHOOL IN THE BIG PINE

THE BLUE JAY

Dear Pussy Cousin:

How true the saying is—"Listeners never hear any good of themselves."

Judge Robin, Bill Grackle and Miss Wren, the teacher at the bird school, were discussing what the birds were going to do about the Blue Jay family, coming to live on the farm.

"They are such thieves," said Miss Wren, "that they will upset the whole school."

I looked up and there was Mr. Blue Jay sitting on a white birch tree listening to what they were saying.

I was glad to hear Bill Grackle say, "A great deal of this disturbance in the neighborhood is nothing but idle gossip. Mr. and Mrs. Jay have come here to the farm to make it their home and I for one am glad to welcome them. They are very beautiful birds and have two lovely bird children."

I think that the blue jay was ashamed of himself to be listening for he flew away.

"When a community starts to shun a neighbor," said Bill, "everyone begins to gossip about him. The poor little blue jays cannot play with the other bird children who would make them better birds."

"Now let us try an experiment," said Bill, "to welcome Mr. and Mrs. Blue Jay and their family as one of us. This will do more to develop the right side of the blue jay's character than anything else that we could do, for it will place them on their honor."

All this happened about a month ago, Cousin Ted.

No one has shunned them and at an entertainment at the bird school the two little jays did their dance.

"Did you ever see a blue jay dance, Cousin Ted, with its tail up and its head down and the funny trum, trum, to which it keeps perfect step? It does a sort of clog dance, keeping in perfect time to the trum, trum, of its bird notes."

Mr. Jay was so pleased when my mistress said that she was glad that the blue jays had come; for their coloring as they flit from tree to tree is so beautiful and their shrill screech, as they talk back and forth to one another is appreciated by the true bird lover, who understands what they say.

Mr. and Mrs. Blue Jay are not particular as to the kind of tree or bush that they select in which to build their nest. They build a bulky ragged nest of twigs, roots, rags, or string.

Mrs. Blue Jay lays from three to six greenish eggs, spotted with brown.

The young birds are very helpless at first, without down or feathers. When about ten days old, their eyes open. They

MR. BLUE JAY WAS LISTENING

are ready to leave the nest when about eighteen days old. They grow very rapidly in size and it is a funny sight to see these baby birds almost as large as their mother and father, but long-legged and gawky, being fed by their parents; stretching open their mouths and emitting their shrill squawk most of the time.

The blue jay is found throughout the United States.

Its color is blue on the upper parts, tinged with purple; the head is crested, the under parts are greyish white, with a black line across the breast. The neck and forehead are black. The wings and tail are blue, barred with black.

So we have now added to the bird colony on the farm this happy family of blue jays, and they are honest, too.

Good night, Chum.

THE HERMIT CRAB

Dear Pussy Cousin:

"What is a hermit crab?" asked Jack this morning.

"Go get Millie and I will tell you all about it," said my mistress.

"Hermit crabs are found in rocky pools on all of the sea coasts. They live in the deserted shells of sea snails, whelks, etc. Their bodies are adapted to this mode of life, for they have no hard shell. The abdomen is soft and is wound in a spiral shape, which fits snugly in the shell that the crab selects for its home," said my mistress. "The tail is not used for swimming, but is supplied with a curved hook with suckers which holds the crab so fast that it will tear apart before it can be pulled out."

"It is comical to see the hermit crab draw into its shell when frightened and cover the entrance with its big claw. This blocks the doorway so that no enemy can reach its soft body," said my mistress.

"One of the most unusual scenes that I witnessed on the beach was a meeting between two hermit crabs," said my mistress. "They evidently discussed the matter of changing houses with each other and could not agree. Suddenly they both spied an empty snail shell which each decided to have for its new home, as it thought that it would fit it better than the shell it occupied. They fought for the possession of this empty snail shell and as Chum and I could not stand the battle any longer, we started towards them. One was frightened at our approach and drew back into its own shell, while the other loosened its hold upon its old shell house and quickly transferred itself to the snail shell, as much as to say, 'Possession is nine points of the law.' "

"I drew back, picked Chum up in my arms and held him while we waited to see what would happen next," said my mistress. "The abandoned shell of the hermit crab lay empty in the pool while Mr. Hermit Crab, in his new dwelling, waved his feelers and sedately crawled away to a safe distance."

"Out came the other hermit crab and took possession of the abandoned shell. It then settled down in its new dwelling as contentedly as though it had never battled for its possession," said my mistress.

"One of the interesting things that the hermit crab does is to detach the sea anemone from its old shell and transfer it to its new home. The sting of the sea anemone protects the hermit crab from its enemies, while the crab carries the sea anemone about, enabling it to get an abundance of food," said my mistress.

You remember, Cousin Ted, I wrote you how the ordinary crab sometimes plants pieces of sponge upon its shell, as the peculiar odor of the living sponge is so offensive to most of the sea people that they will not come near the crab.

The hermit crab feeds upon carrion, vegetable matter, small fish and mollusks.

"I am sorry to say," said my mistress, "that these hermit crabs have a quarrelsome disposition and constantly try to rob each other of their shell houses."

THE HERMIT CRAB IN ITS SHELL HOUSE

"There is one species who rents a room in its shell house to a sea worm. This crab gets very angry at its tenant when the sea worm puts out its head and snatches a bit of food away from the crab, as it frequently does. Otherwise the crab seems to think that the tenant is a desirable one," said my mistress.

"There is a large species of hermit crab which is found far from the water in the tropics. Its name is the Diogenes Crab, and it uses the cocoanut shell for its home," said my mistress.

"I can hardly wait," said Millie, "to go to the seashore this summer to study all of these wonderful things."

Good night,
Chum.

FOSSILS

Dear Pussy Cousin:

Are you not glad that we did not live during the remote age, when the volcanic eruptions came and buried the animals and turned them into stone?

I should hate to be a stone pussy, would not you?

It was very interesting to hear about it when my master and mistress were talking last night.

This volcanic ash comes down and settles upon the earth and covers everything. Even things as frail as the maidenhair fern. They are covered up and are gradually pressed down layer upon layer until they are turned into stone, leaving their impressions, which are called fossils.

One of the fossil specimens that my master has is a crinoid. This word is Greek for lily. This crinoid lived hundreds of years ago at the bottom of the sea.

One of these fossil crinoids was found in the center of the United States where workmen were digging a cellar. This discovery seems to indicate that at one time this section of the country was at the bottom of the sea.

"What are crinoids?" asked Jack.

"The crinoid consists of a head on a slender stalk of calcareous disks which are connected so as to allow considerable freedom of motion," said my mistress. "The head is like a flower or lily, with waving arms or tentacles and a mouth in the center."

"Do you mean that a crinoid is not a real flower, but is an animal?" interrupted Jack.

"Yes, it is called the sea lily on account of its form, but it is really a living animal. The tentacles that form the flower are its arms," said my mistress. "The fossil remains of the crinoid are often mistaken for fossil starfish."

Kansas and Missouri are rich in fossils and many wonderful specimens have been found in these two states.

These crinoids are also found in the Mississippi valley, but, very few have the head, as it was so soft and fragile that it was usually ground to a powder, although the stems are commonly found.

"The impressions of the maiden-hair fern are found in some of the rocks," said my mistress. "Millie, you have no idea of the delicate tracery of these fossils. Every little vein of the maiden-hair fern leaf shows in these fossil specimens."

"You know, Millie, I told you the other day that man's brain could create a great deal, but if he is a close observer of nature, he will get far more beautiful designs from her than he could possibly create," said my mistress.

My mistress laid her hand upon my head and said, "During the volcanic eruptions in the past ages many plants and animals, whose fossil remains are now found, were buried. These fossils show us that animals were then much larger than ours are now."

"Do you suppose that Chum's big paws go back to that age?" said Jack.

As I said in the beginning of this letter, it is all very interesting, but I am glad that I did not live in those times when the volcanic eruptions came and buried both the plants and animals, for I want to be a real live pussy and not a stone one.

Good night,
Chum.

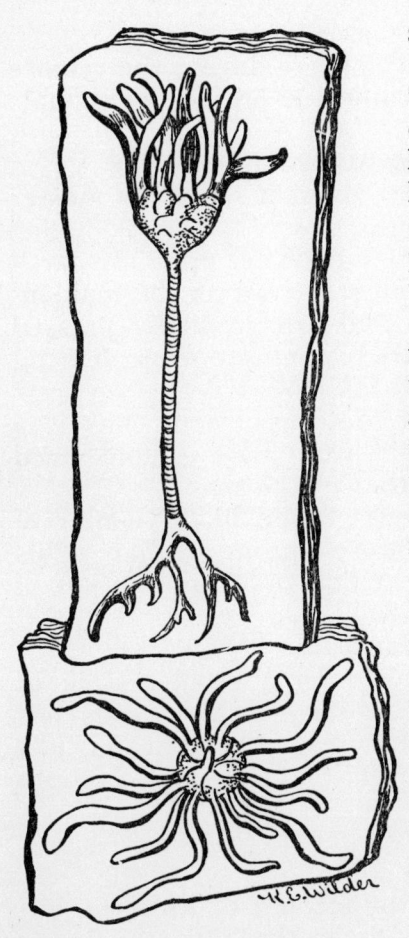

FOSSIL CRINOID AND HEAD OF CRINOID

THE BAT

Dear Pussy Cousin:

Mary was sitting on the back porch. My mistress asked her if she would like to go down to the garden with us to see the flowers.

"Indeed I would, if I can get back before the bats come out," she answered.

"Why Mary, you are not afraid of a bat, are you?" asked my mistress.

"Indeed I am. When a mouse takes to wings and wraps them around itself like the cloak of a monk, it is time that every Christian should be on guard against the critter," said Mary.

"Mary, don't be foolish," said my mistress. "Bats are harmless and very beneficial in clearing the night air of mosquitoes, gnats and other insects. Come over to the summer house in the garden and I will tell you and the children all about the bat. I am quite sure that you will be ashamed for being afraid of this interesting little animal.

"The bat is a small furry animal with membranous wings. In its power of flight it resembles the birds and the insects. On the light frame of the wings is stretched a tough, leathery, hairless skin. These wings are controlled by strong muscles which enable the bat to fly about as easily as a bird," said my mistress.

"What Mary meant by its wrapping its cloak about it like a monk was that the bat folds its wings about its body while resting," said my mistress.

"The old English and German name for the bat is 'flitter mouse,' because of its strong resemblence to a mouse. Its little body is covered with fur just like that of a mouse," said my mistress.

"The most distinctive thing about a bat is its large ears. Its hearing is very acute. The ears may be folded down in some species," said my mistress.

"Bats prefer a warm climate, although they are generally distributed throughout the world. They like to congregate in great numbers in a favored locality," said my mistress.

"The hooks on its fingers are very useful to the bat, for it hangs itself up by them. It also hangs itself up by its feet for its winter sleep, when it remains in a torpid state," said my mistress. "These feet are provided with hooked nails."

"Its body does look like a mouse, for it is covered with fine fur; but the membranous skin which covers the wings is hairless and as tough as leather. The bat catches so many insects while it is flying through the air at night that it is considered of great benefit to man. It makes its home in a cave or hollow tree, or suspends itself from the branch of a densely shaded tree," said my mistress.

"Another thing that I am going to tell you that will surprise you, Mary, is that the old saying, 'blind as a bat,' is misapplied, for the bat has two very bright, beady eyes. They are nearly buried in its soft fur, but the bat sees many people who are foolish enough to be afraid of it," said my mistress.

"Bats fly about with their young clinging to them," said my mistress.

"Well," said Mary, "a bat may be very useful to clear the air of insects at night, but I have no respect for any mother that will go flying around at night with her babies clinging to her. She should stay at home and keep her babies there, instead of gallivanting around through the air."

My mistress and the children laughed.

Jack picked me up in his arms, gave me a hug, and said, "Chum is more interested in nature and would make a much better scientist than Mary."

Good night,
Chum.

HOW COFFEE GROWS

Dear Pussy Cousin:

Jack asked my mistress, at the breakfast table this morning, "How does coffee grow?"

My mistress drew a branch of the coffee tree in blossom that showed how the bean forms, and told how it grew.

She said that the Arabian coffee comes from a shrub fifteen to eighteen feet high. Its leaves are from three to four inches long, borne in pairs on slender branches. The flowers occur in clusters of from four to sixteen. They are white and fragrant. The fruits or "cherries" are first a dark green, changing to yellow, then to red, and when thoroughly ripe to a dark crimson. The outer portion is fleshy like a cherry. Each fruit contains two seeds covered by a dry, smooth, straw-colored husk. The seed is horny. This seed is the unroasted coffee bean. Between each seed is a thin covering known as the "silver skin". The two beans which each fruit contains lie with their flat sides together.

Coffee thrives best in a hot, moist climate. In the coffee-growing districts of Brazil, the difference in climate has great influence on the quality of the coffee.

It takes seven months from the blossoming to the ripening of the fruit.

The coffee beans are stripped from the branches by hand and are collected in baskets. The green and unripe beans are left to be picked later.

The Arabs allow the fruit to mature fully and to fall of their own accord, a cloth being spread under the tree to catch them. In this way only the ripe fruit is collected, a fact which accounts for the excellent quality of Mocha coffee.

In Brazil the ground is cleared of weeds and the cherries are allowed to fall. They are then gathered and spread on drying grounds, being stirred frequently to allow them all to be exposed to the sun. The pulpy covering ferments and dries out in about two weeks. When thoroughly dried, the beans can be stored for any length of time. Before being shipped, the dry pulp is removed by pounding in a mortar. The beans are thus freed from the husk.

The bean is thoroughly roasted before being used, and when ground gives the wonderful aroma with which we are all familiar.

When I smell the coffee boiling in the morning, I do not wonder that people want to drink it.

Good night,
Chum.

HOW COFFEE GROWS—SHOWING FLOWER, CHERRY AND BEAN

THE MONARCH BUTTERFLY

Dear Pussy Cousin:

We all went out and found a big clump of milkweed growing in the field. There on one of the flowers was a Monarch butterfly. Its wings were beautiful as they gleamed in the sun.

"Why is it that you never see the Monarch butterfly until the milkweed is in blossom?" asked Millie.

"I am glad that you asked me that question," said my mistress. "I have been watching for the Monarch butterfly, so that I could show you children how interesting it is. It pleases me very much, Millie, to think that you have observed that it only appears when the milkweed is in bloom. The reason is that the female lays her eggs on the milkweed leaves."

The male is a gorgeously colored butterfly. The upper surface of the wings is a copper brown, with black veins and a deep border of black, with white spots around the edge.

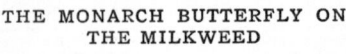

THE MONARCH BUTTERFLY ON THE MILKWEED

He is well named, being "monarch of all he surveys," for no bird will touch him or his caterpillar.

The male butterfly has scent scales on each hind wing, to attract his lady love. She is also brilliant in color but has no scent scales.

This butterfly is repulsive to birds in both its caterpillar and butterfly stages, so that it can feed and fly about boldly without fear of being destroyed.

The Monarch butterfly lived in its native tropics until its food plants were insufficient to nourish the increasing numbers, so it began going further north and south during the period of plant growth.

The mother butterfly follows the milkweed northward and deposits her eggs. They hatch and these butterflies continue the journey. Thus late in the season they are found as far north as Hudson Bay.

As cold weather approaches, these butterflies gather in great flocks and fly back to the south.

The Monarch is the strongest flyer of all the butterflies. It has been found far out at sea. People on ships have seen it five hundred miles from shore. It has reached Europe either by flying or as a stowaway on a ship.

"You say that the Monarch butterfly migrates just as the birds do?" asked Millie.

"Yes, and it lives for two years," said my mistress.

The caterpillar of the Monarch butterfly is gay looking and makes no attempt to hide at the approach of a bird, for it seems to know that the birds will not touch it.

The Monarch butterfly raises only one brood in the north during the summer, but several in the south.

I shall tell my friend the swallow-tail butterfly all that I have learned from my mistress about the Monarch butterfly.

Good night,
Chum.

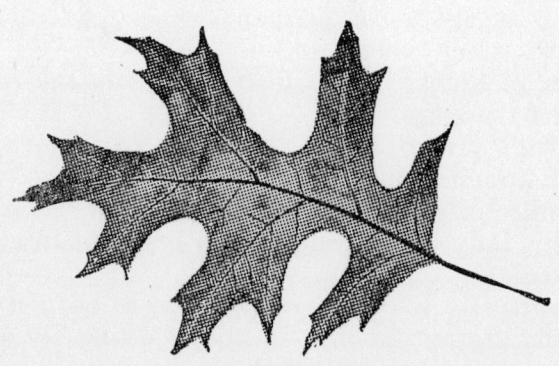

CURLEY AND THE BUTTERNUT TREE

Dear Pussy Cousin:

This morning Curley, the grey squirrel, asked me to go to the top of the hill where the butternut tree grows. It is a big tree and is loaded with butternuts. When we reached the hill, Curley said, "Let us race to the top." We did and he beat me. When I arrived he was on one of the branches talking to the tree.

The butternut tree said, "Curley, you are not going to carry off any of these butternuts, because you are fed all winter by your mistress. The squirrels in the woods are depending on me to provide them with food."

"You need not worry," I said, "Curley is too lazy to tote those great big butternuts way down to his house."

"Chum is right. I am lazy," said Curley. "My mistress provides nuts for me all winter. I have not gathered one."

The butternut tree told us that it was worried about the family of grey squirrels that live up in the woods. Every year they depend upon nuts for their winter supply of food.

One of the grey squirrels caught his foot in a trap last week and almost tore it off. He is up in his nest and cannot walk.

This morning the chipmunk told me that the grey squirrel's mother had been caught and that her foot is in a very serious condition. That leaves only one squirrel to carry enough nuts to last them through the winter, but before he can carry enough the children will have gathered all of the butternuts. So the squirrels will suffer.

Curley sat very quiet. Then he scratched his ear and said, "I tell you what we will do. You roll these nuts to the side of the hill with your big paw and then give them a push, and down they will go. When they get to the bottom, I will carry them to the grey squirrel's nest."

So I pushed the butternuts with my big paw to the edge of the hill. I then stood back a little and gave them a whack and down they rolled.

Curley scampered down the hill after the nuts.

"Be careful of the trap, Curley," I said.

"I see it," said Curley. "The squirrels have uncovered it."

After rolling the butternuts down I stopped to rest.

"You must be lonely on top of this hill without another tree anywhere near," I said to the butternut tree.

"I am, Chum," the butternut tree said. "I wish the boys and girls that gather the nuts would leave one or two so I would have some young trees around me for company."

"I believe that I could plant some of those nuts for you with my big paw," I said.

I dug a hole, pushed one of the nuts into it, scratched the earth over it, and patted it down with my big paws. I planted several nuts in this way.

"That is great, Chum," said the butternut tree. "I will be so interested to see those nuts sprout. I will guard and protect them with my branches until they grow to be big trees."

That afternoon my mistress and I went for a walk. I told Bill Grackle and Curley to stand near the squirrel's tree where the trap was set. Curley chattered and Bill made his noise like an old rusty hinge, while I mewed. This noise attracted the attention of my mistress, who came to the tree to see what the trouble was and found the trap. She was very angry.

"These traps may catch our pets as well as the wild animals," she said to the farmer.

He worked all day printing signs to keep people from setting traps on his property.

So you see, between us, that morning, Curley and I made the squirrels and the butternut tree happy, and helped to prevent the poor little animals of the woods from being caught in those cruel traps.

We are going to visit the squirrels every day. Curley will bring them nuts to help fill the old hollow tree, so they will have enough food for the winter.

Good night,
Chum.

CANADIAN THISTLE

THE CLAM FAMILY

Dear Pussy Cousin:

Last night when the clam chowder was served, Millie asked my mistress how clams lived. She told Millie that she would show her when they were at the beach next summer.

That made me think, Cousin Ted, that I never wrote you about the little girl that my mistress invited from the hotel to go down to the beach with her last summer to see how the clams lived.

My mistress took a spade, dug a hole in the sand, and found two clams side by side. She tapped near one with her spade and it spouted water. You can always tell whether there are any clams, when you are walking along the beach, by the tiny holes in the sand through which they get air. The clams spout water through these holes like a little fountain when you walk near them.

My mistress took a hard shell clam, a cohog clam, a frilled venus clam and a razor clam and laid the shells together on the beach, which showed us the difference between them.

A RAZOR CLAM, A FRILLED VENUS CLAM,
A COHOG CLAM, AND A HARD SHELL CLAM

The clam that spouted water was still different. It was a soft shell clam.

It was a very interesting morning. I told the starfish what I had learned about the clams.

That was the morning that the starfish came up to tell me about the wonderful seaweed.

"Take your big paw and scratch those long, black rolls of sea grass that you see washed up on the beach," it said. "You will find some wonderful shells that are caught in the seaweed and washed up on the beach with it."

My mistress mailed Mrs. S. a box of the different clam shells. Do you remember seeing them?

Good night,
Chum.

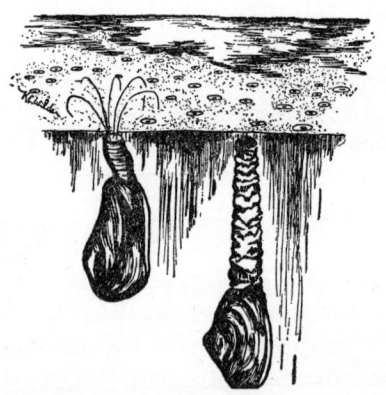

MY MISTRESS DUG DOWN IN THE SAND
TO SHOW HOW THE CLAMS LIVED

HOW SEEDS TRAVEL

Dear Pussy Cousin:

This is what Bill Grackle told me this morning.

I said to him, "Billy, how do seeds travel?"

"Why, Chum, we birds carry a great many, and the animals carry some, for the burry ones stick to their fur; but the wind is the greatest seed bearer of us all."

"I do not know what the seeds would do if it were not for the wind," said Bill.

"It is wonderful, Chum, to see how the seeds have wings. When I was a little bird I thought that the birch seeds were small birds flying in the air. My mother laughed at me and said, 'Why Billy! those are not birds. They are seeds. If you look closely you will see seeds blowing about almost every month of the year.'"

Billy showed me a birch and a maple seed. They both had wings, but the maple seed is at the base of each wing. The wind catches their little sails and carries them away.

Then there is the cottonwood tree which blows its fine feathery seed through the air, making one think of snow flakes.

Many seeds have a sharp point on the heavy end, so that when they fall they stick into the ground and sprout quickly. If they lay on top of the ground they would have to depend upon the rain to wash the dirt over them.

"The most wonderful thing of all to me, Chum," said Billy, "is the way the pine holds its seed, one under each petal of the pine cone. When the seeds are ripe the petals of the cone open, the seeds drop out, and are scattered by the wind. When they fall to the ground and sprout, each seed grows into a tree, and this is how the pine forest starts."

Curley came along and said, "What are you fellows talking about?"

"THE BIRCH SEEDS LOOK LIKE LITTLE BIRDS FLYING THROUGH THE AIR," SAID BILLY GRACKLE

"How seeds travel," I said.

Bill then said, "If those acorns are allowed to remain on the ground they will take root and make oak trees; that is, if the squirrels don't get them first."

Curley looked up at him and said, "How about the chestnut burrs? Does not the frost open them and let the chestnuts drop out for the squirrels so that we don't have to touch the prickly things—showing that they want us to eat them?"

"Now look here, Bill Grackle, we squirrels do as much good in carrying around the nuts and dropping them here and there as you birds do with the seeds, so don't be quite so conceited," said Curley.

I could not help laughing at the expression on Curley's face as he winked at me and said: "The birds eat just as many seeds as the squirrels eat nuts!" And off he scampered.

Bill and I just sat there and laughed.

So that is how seeds travel.

Good night,
Chum.

THE CROW AND THE CORN

Dear Pussy Cousin:

The crow asked me to come with him this morning. I could see by the way he acted that something had made him very angry.

I followed him and he flew straight to the corn field. When I arrived, he was sitting with his back turned to a huge hill of corn.

"Chum, how would you feel if you were responsible for such a wonderful hill of corn as that and did not get the credit for it?"

"Why, what do you mean, Mr. Crow?" I asked.

"I mean that the farmer who planted this field of corn, with the help of his half grown boy, threw from twelve to fifteen kernels in each hill," said the crow.

"My entire family worked for three consecutive mornings, going after them picking out the corn. Do you suppose that if it were not for us the farmer would have had any such crop of corn?" asked the crow.

"Because of so many kernels being in a hill, the plants would have come up crowded. Each one would have fought the other for its existence and they all would have become puny. Realizing this, and knowing that there was to be a contest among the farmers, I called a special meeting of the crows. The farmer fed us in the spring, so we decided to give him the benefit of all our corn knowledge to help him grow the finest crop of corn in this county.

"I personally ate all but three of the kernels of corn that he put in this hill. And you see the result. Why, it is the most wonderful hill of corn that could possibly be grown," said the crow.

"Each plant that came up had all of the nourishment that it needed, while if I had left the ten or twelve kernels, they would all have come up little spindling things, and none of them would have had enough to eat," said the crow. "It makes me so angry, Chum, not to have the credit for this fine corn that I have to turn my back. I can not look at it."

As I looked up, I thought that I had never seen such a wonderful hill of corn. It grew so high and the stalks were so thick and healthy. The ears of corn were so full of kernels that they were ready to burst from the shock.

"How is it that the corn husks are all pulled back?" I asked.

"The inspector was here this morning and the farmer showed him the corn," said the crow.

"The inspector told the farmer that he had visited eight farms so far this week and no crop compared with this one. He said that he had never seen anything as perfect and advised him to enter it at the state fair. He said he was quite sure that it would get first prize," said the crow.

"As the inspector left the field, he slapped the farmer on the back and said, 'Well, you certainly beat

AS I LOOKED UP I THOUGHT THAT I HAD NEVER SEEN SUCH A WONDERFUL HILL OF CORN

the crows that time.'" When the crow said this he looked so funny that I burst out laughing. I was very sorry that I did so, because he looked so indignantly at me.

"Pardon me, Mr. Crow," I said, "but you looked so funny."

"We all have to go through life doing things that make other people successful, without getting any credit for it. You have no idea how many times I see people who do kind and wonderful things for others but never even get thanked," I told the crow.

"We should not do things to get credit, Mr. Crow," I said. "We should do what we can every day to help others, because we want to see them succeed."

He hung his head for several minutes, then looked up at me and said, "Chum, I believe you are right. That is the trouble with half of the people in this world. They only do things for others so that they may be praised for it. I never realized that before."

"Say, do you know what I intend to do?" said the crow. "I am going to help that farmer next year and I shall not expect credit for it, either."

"Goodby, Chum, thank you for your good advice," said the crow as he flew away.

I wish you and Aunt Polly could have seen this wonderful hill of corn.

Good night,
Chum.

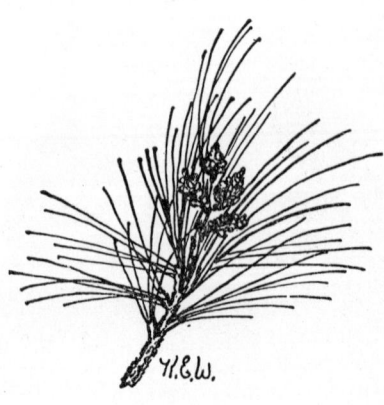

INDEX

	Page
ANT COWS	94
ANTS, PARASOL	3
AUTUMN RACE	100
BAT, THE	176
BEE'S BREAD BASKET	115
BIRD SCHOOL, EXAMINATION AT THE	104
BULBS GROW, HOW	131
BUTTERFLY, THE MONARCH	180
BUTTERNUT TREE, CURLEY AND THE	182
CADDICE FLY, THE	28
CICADA OR SEVENTEEN-YEAR LOCUST	111
CLAM FAMILY	185
CLOVER, THE	40
COCOA BEAN, THE	13
COFFEE GROWS, HOW	178
COTTON GROWS, HOW	10
COTTONWOOD, THE	19
COW AND THE CALF, THE	25
CRAB, THE HERMIT	172
CRAB, THE HORSESHOE	162
CROW AND THE CORN	190
CUCKOO, THE YELLOW-BILLED	165
DAHLIAS	144
DAISY	5
DANDELION, THE	148
DRAGON FLY	137
EARTHWORM	125
FAN, THE SEA	77
FIRE FLIES	98
FOSSILS	174
FROG, THE HOP TOAD AND THE TREE TOAD	46
GALL HOUSES	70
GENTIAN, THE FRINGED	32
GRACKLE, BRONZE	63
HEMP	158
HERON, THE GREAT BLUE	121
HUMMING BIRD, THE RUBY-THROATED	152
JACK-IN-THE-PULPIT	160
JAY, THE BLUE	170
KINGFISHER, THE	89
KITTENS AND THE BREAD	56

INDEX—Continued

	Page
LEAF BUD	135
MALLOW, ROSE	102
MALLOW, MARSH	117
MOLD	68
MOUSE AND HER HOME, MRS. MEADOW	48
ORIOLE, BALTIMORE	42
PANSY AND THE BEE	59
PELICAN, THE	21
RATS, THE ACCOMMODATING	141
REDWOODS, THE	1
ROBINS, THE	65
RUBBER	107
SEED, WHAT ONE SHOULD KNOW ABOUT A	166
SEEDS TRAVEL, HOW	187
SEEDS, WHEN WE PLANT	168
SHARK'S EGG, THE	31
SILKWORM, THE	113
SNAILS, THE	61
SNAIL, THE VIOLET	81
SPARROW, THE LTTLE	15
SPICES	36
SPIDERS BALLOONING	96
SPIDER, JIMMY	26
SPIDER, THE TRAP-DOOR	39
SPONGE, THE CUP	73
STALACTITES, HOW FORMED	8
SWORDFISH, THE	119
SUGAR BEET, THE	17
SUGAR, MAPLE	128
TADPOLES AND THE MOSQUITOES	154
TEA	142
THIEF, THE CREAM	123
TREE HOPPERS, THE	34
TUMBLE BUG, THE	7
TURTLE, THE CURIOSITY OF MRS.	91
VILLAGE, THE DESERTED	109
WARBLER, THE WORM-EATING	84
WASPS, MINER	157
WASPS, MUD	78
WASPS, PAPER	44
WOOD, FORMATION OF GRAIN IN	52
WOODPECKER, RED-HEADED	150
WOODPECKER, DOWNY	146
WORM, THE UGLY	86
YEAST PLANT, THE	54